Eagan Press Handbook Series

# Sweeteners: Alternative

## Amy L. Nelson

eagan press
St. Paul, Minnesota, USA

Cover: Center image courtesy of McNeil Specialty Products Company;
beverages courtesy of Virginia Dare; angel food cake, hard candy,
and molded gelatin, ©1997 Artville LLC; and Summit™ HPLC System
courtesy of Dionex.

Library of Congress Catalog Card Number: 99-67246
International Standard Book Number: 1-891127-11-X

Printed in the United States of America on acid-free paper

American Association of Cereal Chemists
3340 Pilot Knob Road
St. Paul, Minnesota 55121-2097, USA

## About the Eagan Press Handbook Series

The Eagan Press Handbook series was developed for food industry practitioners. It offers a practical approach to understanding the basics of food ingredients, applications, and processes—whether the reader is a research chemist wanting practical information compiled in a single source or a purchasing agent trying to understand product specifications. The handbook series is designed to reach a broad readership; the books are not limited to a single product category but rather serve professionals in all segments of the food processing industry and their allied suppliers.

In developing this series, Eagan Press recognized the need to fill the gap between the highly fragmented, theoretical, and often not readily available information in the scientific literature and the product-specific information available from suppliers. It enlisted experts in specific areas to contribute their expertise to the development and fruition of this series.

The content of the books has been prepared in a rigorous manner, including substantial peer review and editing, and is presented in a user friendly format with definitions of terms, examples, illustrations, and trouble-shooting tips. The result is a set of practical guides containing information useful to those involved in product development, production, testing, ingredient purchasing, engineering, and marketing aspects of the food industry.

## Acknowledgment of Sponsors for *Sweeteners: Alternative*

Eagan Press would like to thank the following companies for their financial support of this handbook:

Cerestar USA, Inc.
Hammond, IN
800/348-9896

McNeil Specialty Products Company
New Brunswick, NJ
732/524-6336

Nutrinova Inc.
Somerset, NJ
800/786-3833

Eagan Press has designed this handbook series as practical guides serving the interests of the food industry as a whole rather than the individual interests of any single company. Nonetheless, corporate sponsorship has allowed these books to be more affordable for a wide audience.

# Acknowledgments

Eagan Press thanks the following individuals for their contributions to the preparation of this book:

Abe Bakal, ABIC International Consultants, Fairfield, NJ

Ross Craig, Danisco Cultor, Ardsley, NY

Carl Jaundoo, Roquette America, Inc., Keokuk, IA

Carolyn M. Merkel, McNeil Specialty Products Company, New Brunswick, NJ

Susan Milovanovic, Burr Ridge, IL

Lyn O'Brien Nabors, Calorie Control Council, Atlanta, GA

Rudi Van Mol, Nutrinova, Somerset, NJ

---

## Books in the Eagan Press Ingredient Handbook Series

| | |
|---|---|
| *Colorants* | *Fats & Oils* |
| *Dairy-Based Ingredients* | *Starches* |
| *Emulsifiers* | *Sweeteners: Alternative* |
| *Enzymes* | *Sweeteners: Nutritive* |

To order any Eagan Press publication call:
TOLL FREE 1-800-328-7560
Monday – Friday, 8:00 a.m. – 4:30 p.m. (Central Time)
in the United States and most of Canada
Elsewhere +1-651-454-7250

Please have your credit card ready and provide this code
to the Eagan Press Customer Service Representative: 7265CK

# Contents

# Sweeteners: Alternative

# Overview

Sweetened foods occupy a large portion of the space on grocery store shelves worldwide. Products ranging from cookies to soft drinks are available to satisfy the consumer's desire for sweetness. Nutritive sweeteners include *sucrose*, corn syrups, *dextrose*, and honey. These sweeteners play other important roles in foods as well. For example, they provide texture, stability, and color. However, increasing concerns about obesity, dental caries, and diabetes as well as the cost of these sweeteners have caused food processors to look for other types of sweetening agents.

There are several approved and several unapproved, nonnutritive, alternative sweeteners. Some are synthetic, and some are found in nature and isolated and purified for use in the food industry. One of the earliest and most widely known synthetic sweeteners is saccharin, which was developed more than a century ago and first used in food products during the early 1900s. Although its use has sparked controversy and debate over the years, it continues to be added to food products throughout the world. Since the introduction of saccharin, the quest for low-cost, effective, alternative sweetening agents has continued in many research laboratories. Many published reports, ranging from discussions on toxicology and carcinogenicity to chemical properties and applications of both approved and unapproved sweetening agents, are readily available (1–3). The alternative sweetening agents used in food products are discussed in this book, with special emphasis on those approved for use in the majority of countries around the world.

## Approval Processes

The entire approval process for a newly developed food additive is complicated and can take several years. Further complicating matters is the fact that different countries have different governmental structures and approval systems for food additives, and certain international organizations also review and approve food ingredients. In general, the manufacturer is responsible for petitioning the various regulatory agencies for approval of its product. Although each country and agency has its own individual requirements, some common terminology exits and most require the following information for the approval process:

**In This Chapter:**

Approval Processes

History and Description

Synthetic Alternative Sweeteners
  Saccharin
  Cyclamate
  Aspartame
  Alitame
  Acesulfame Potassium
  Sucralose

Naturally Occurring High-Intensity Sweeteners
  Thaumatins
  Glycyrrhizin
  Stevioside

Sugar Alcohols

**Sucrose**—A 12-carbon disaccharide, composed of one molecule of glucose and one of fructose, obtained from sugar cane and sugar beets; the primary sweetener in the world.

**Dextrose**—A six-carbon sugar; also called glucose.

- Name, identity, and characteristics (e.g., stability and chemical properties) of the substance
- Food categories in which the substance can be used
- Maximum usage levels and expected consumption information
- Methods and results of safety investigations (e.g., toxicological studies)
- Labeling requirements

The United States also requires information about the impact the substance may have on the environment.

In the United States, food additives are regulated by the 1958 Food Additives Amendment to the 1938 Food, Drug and Cosmetic Act. This amendment requires that additives used in foods go through an approval process prior to their use. Two types of additives are exempt from the amendment: 1) those that were accepted as safe prior to the 1958 amendment and 2) those described as Generally Recognized as Safe (*GRAS*), that is, additives considered safe by experts on the basis of their history of use in foods. However, a substance (e.g., saccharin) can lose its GRAS status if new research finds it to be unsafe. The *Delaney Clause*, a significant part of the U.S. Food Additives Amendment, states that additives found to cause cancer in humans or animals cannot be approved for use in foods. Manu-

**TABLE 1-1.** Acceptable Daily Intakes (ADIs) of High-Intensity Sweeteners (mg/kg of body weight per day)

| Sweetener | JECFA[a] | FDA[b] |
|---|---|---|
| Acesulfame K | 9 | 15 |
| Aspartame | 40 | 50 |
| Cyclamate | 11 | Not permitted |
| Saccharin | 5 | Not established |
| Alitame | 15 | Not established |
| Sucralose | 15 | 5 |

[a] Joint Expert Committee on Food Additives.
[b] U.S. Food and Drug Administration.

**GRAS**—Generally Recognized as Safe. Pertains to food additives that experts have declared safe for use in foods on the basis of their history of use.

**Delaney Clause**—A clause in the 1958 Food Additives Amendment forbidding the use of a substance in food if, after appropriate tests, any part of it was shown to cause cancer in humans or animals.

**Box 1.1. Common Terminology**

**NOEL:** No Observable Effect Level (also sometimes called the NOAEL, No Observable Adverse Effect Level, or NAEL, No Adverse Effect Level); the maximum level of a substance used in animal feeding studies in which no toxicological or adverse effects (e.g., weight gain or weight loss of body or organs) were found.

**ADI:** Acceptable Daily Intake; an estimate of the amount of a substance that can be ingested daily that is not anticipated to result in adverse effects (the definition was established by the U.N. World Health Organization, Food and Agriculture Organization). The ADI is based on the NOEL as

$$ADI = NOEL/100$$

The units are expressed as milligrams per kilograms of body weight per day. The factor of 100 is a safety factor. The ADI is a generalization that is used as a guideline. It is not intended to represent a maximum dosage where there is a clearly safe or unsafe dosage. The ADIs for the sweeteners discussed here are listed in Table 1-1.

facturers using approved additives must abide by Good Manufacturing Practices (*GMPs*), which place a general limit on additive usage by stating that the amount used can be only that which achieves the desired effect.

Among the most frequent topics of debate and investigation is the safety of alternative sweeteners and of the decomposition products that may form during processing or storage. Even after a complete approval process, several food ingredients (e.g., saccharin and cyclamate) have had their approval or GRAS status revoked in the United States. Approval can be reinstated if research provides new information.

## History and Description

Alternative sweeteners can be categorized in several ways, including by their

- Chemical nature (synthetic versus naturally occurring)
- Applicability (i.e., whether they are heat stable, pH stable, etc.)
- Level of intensity (compared with the sweetening power of sucrose)
- Chronological use (newly approved, used for 20 years, etc.)
- Type of applications (e.g., low-calorie foods)
- Acceptability (approved versus unapproved)

In this chapter, histories and descriptions of the most widely recognized alternative sweeteners and sugar alcohols are reviewed in terms of their chemical natures. In the product application chapters, the discussion focuses on alternative sweeteners in terms of the other categories. For a review of the less common alternative sweeteners (e.g., *monoterpenoids*, derivatives of urea, etc.), the book by Krutosikova and Uher (2) is recommended.

## Synthetic Alternative Sweeteners

The development of synthetic sweeteners began in the chemical industry during the late nineteenth century. The first sweetener synthesized for mass production was saccharin. Several companies then began devoting at least part of their research programs to the development of alternative sweeteners. Most synthetic sweeteners, however, were discovered accidentally.

### SACCHARIN

**History.** Saccharin is one of the oldest nonnutritive synthetic sweeteners. It was discovered in 1878 in the laboratory of Ira Remsen at Johns Hopkins University in Maryland by Constantin Fahlberg, who was trying to oxidize toluene sulfonamides (1). He discovered that a compound resulting from one of his experiments tasted very sweet. The product was named "saccharin," from "saccharose," a

**GMPs**—Good Manufacturing Practices. The food-handling practices in the United States. They include general limits on the amounts of food additives used so that the total amount is only that which will achieve the desired effect in the food system.

**Monoterpenoid**—A terpene with one isoprene unit in its structure.

chemical name for sucrose. Saccharin was originally produced in New York, but production was moved to Germany under Fahlberg's direction. John Queeny, of Meyer Brothers Drug Company in St. Louis, Missouri, imported saccharin from the German production facility and was very interested in manufacturing the compound. After Meyer Brothers showed no interest, Queeny left the company, received money from the Liquid Carbonic Industries Corporation, and formed the Monsanto Chemical Company. Saccharin has been in use since the early 1900s.

**Description.** The chemical name for saccharin is *o*-benzosulfimide. It is a white, crystalline powder that is 300–600 times sweeter than sucrose. Saccharin is available as acid saccharin, sodium saccharin, and calcium saccharin (Fig. 1-1).

**Legal status.** Saccharin has been one of the most controversial sweeteners for almost a century. Its safety has been reviewed and debated many times. The books *Alternative Sweeteners* and *Natural and Synthetic Sweet Substances* (1,2) contain extensive reviews of saccharin's legal and safety history. Saccharin is approved for use in more than 90 countries. Approved food applications include soft drinks, fruit juices, tabletop sweeteners, chewing gum, and jellies.

The safety controversy is exemplified by saccharin's history in the United States. As early as 1906, there were questions about the safety of saccharin for human consumption. However, President Theodore Roosevelt, who was influential in keeping saccharin's status as an approved food ingredient, was quoted as stating, "Anyone who says saccharin is injurious to health is an idiot!" (4).

In 1977, Canadian research studies indicated an increase in the incidence of bladder tumors in male rats fed saccharin. The U.S. Food and Drug Administration (FDA) was ready to ban the sweetener under the Delaney Clause, but the outcry against its ban was immense. The public had been informed that the results of the studies were questionable because the amount of saccharin fed to the rats was the equivalent of drinking 800–1,000 cans of diet soda per day. Also, the case findings were specific to rats, and since rat bladders are physiologically unique and different from human bladders, there was no proof that saccharin would cause cancer in humans. Congress placed a moratorium on the proposed ban and required that the following statement be printed on the containers of food products made with saccharin: "Use of this product may be hazardous to your health. This product contains saccharin which has been determined to cause cancer in laboratory animals." Subsequent epidemiological studies have not shown a relationship between the ingestion of saccharin and an increase in the risk of cancer in humans. In 1981, saccharin was included in the government's Report on Carcinogens, which includes a list of compounds that are suspected carcinogens. In 1997, removal of saccharin from the list was requested in a peti-

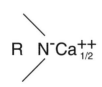

Acid saccharin

Sodium saccharin

Calcium saccharin

**Fig. 1-1.** Chemical structure of saccharin. R = acid saccharin structure.

tion filed by the Calorie Control Council. Numerous scientists, health groups, and regulators supported the removal, which is still under review. In the meantime, saccharin is allowed in the United States with the accompanying warning label.

## CYCLAMATE

**History.** Like other synthetic high-intensity sweeteners, cyclamate was discovered accidentally. In 1937, Michael Sveda, a graduate student at the University of Illinois, was smoking a cigarette after completing some of his laboratory work and noticed that his cigarette tasted sweet (5). He realized that a substance from the laboratory was on his fingers and was affecting the taste of his cigarette. Cyclamate gained in popularity during the 1950s and 1960s and was used primarily in a blend with saccharin. This blend was *synergistic* and improved the taste of products made with saccharin alone.

**Description.** Cyclamate is a white, crystalline powder that is roughly 30 times sweeter than sucrose. Its chemical name is cyclamic acid or cyclohexylsulfamic acid (Fig. 1-2). Cyclamate is generally used in the form of a sodium or calcium salt. Cyclohexylamine, a *metabolite*, is a breakdown product of cyclamate with a bitter taste.

**Legal status.** Cyclamates are approved for use in more than 50 countries in products such as tabletop sweeteners, beverages, processed fruits, chewing gum, candies, and more. The notable exception is the use of cyclamates in the United States. The FDA once listed cyclamates as GRAS substances, and they were used in combination with saccharin in soft drinks and numerous other products. Scientific studies in 1969 reportedly found cyclamates to be a causative agent of malignant bladder tumors in rats. In 1970, cyclamates were removed from the GRAS list and banned. Many countries did not follow suit, and in numerous subsequent studies, cyclamate was not found to be carcinogenic. Abbott Laboratories (the U.S. producer of cyclamate) filed a food additive petition for cyclamate in 1973, but approval was denied in 1980. A second petition was filed by the Calorie Control Council and Abbott Laboratories in 1982, but cyclamate is still banned in the United States.

## ASPARTAME

**History.** In 1965, James Schlatter of G.D. Searle & Co. was synthesizing peptide drugs when he found a sweet-tasting substance on his fingers (1). The compound was given the name "aspartame," a simplification of aspartylphenylalanine methyl ester. G.D. Searle began research into derivatives of aspartame but eventually commercialized aspartame because of its ease of manufacture and taste quality and because it was most likely to pass safety testing and be approved by the FDA (1,2). It is sold

**Synergistic**—Pertaining to the relationship of two or more ingredients, which combined in a food system have a greater total effect than the sum of the individual effects.

**Metabolite**—A substance produced during the metabolism or digestion of a compound.

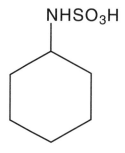

Cyclamic acid (cyclamate)

$NHSO_3^-Na^+$

R

Sodium cyclamate

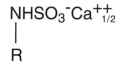

Calcium cyclamate

**Fig. 1-2.** Chemical structure of cyclamate. R = cyclamic acid structure.

under the brand name NutraSweet. Aspartame is recognized by the public as the ingredient used in Equal and other tabletop sweetener packets.

**Description.** Aspartame is a white, crystalline powder that is about 160–220 times sweeter than sucrose. It is made from two amino acid components, L-aspartic acid and L-phenylalanine. The methyl ester occurs on the phenylalanine moiety (Fig. 1-3). The true chemical name is *N*-L-α-aspartyl-L-phenylalanine-1-methyl ester. Under certain conditions, aspartame decomposes into different metabolites and loses its sweetness. These metabolites are discussed in detail in Chapter 2.

**Legal status.** Aspartame is one of the most widely used high-intensity sweeteners available in the marketplace today. It is approved in more than 90 countries for use in numerous applications including tabletop sweeteners, carbonated beverages, frozen desserts, coffee, toppings, and fillings. It was approved in the United States for use in tabletop sweeteners, various foods, and dry beverage mixes in 1981, the first new sweetener approved in more than 25 years. In 1983, it was approved for use in carbonated beverages and currently dominates the U.S. diet soda industry. It was approved as a general-purpose sweetener in the United States in 1996.

Phenylalanine is a component and metabolite of aspartame. Persons born with a condition known as *phenylketonuria* are not able to metabolize phenylalanine. In order to avoid possible brain damage, these people must monitor their dietary intake of this amino acid from all sources. Therefore, products that contain aspartame must be labeled with the warning, "Phenylketonuriacs: contains phenylalanine."

Although there have been public petitions for the removal of aspartame's approved status, the FDA has remained steadfast in allowing its use. It is one of the most widely reviewed and studied food additives, and many scientists and international and national organizations have concluded that on the basis of clinical studies, aspartame and its decomposition products are safe for human consumption.

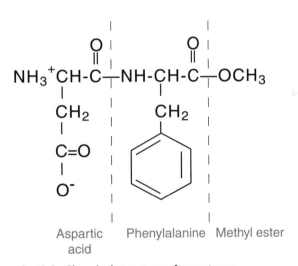

Aspartic acid    Phenylalanine    Methyl ester

**Fig. 1-3.** Chemical structure of aspartame.

**Phenylketonuria**—Inherited metabolic disease characterized by the inability to metabolize phenylalanine, resulting in brain damage.

**Dipeptide**—A combination of two peptides. A peptide is an amide resulting from the condensation of amino acids.

## ALITAME

**History.** After the discovery of aspartame, Pfizer, Inc., researched other potential high-intensity *dipeptide* sweeteners. Alitame was developed from their research effort and patented in 1983 (6).

**Description.** Alitame is formed from the amino acids L-aspartic acid and D-alanine and a novel amine. Its chemical structure is shown in Figure 1-4. It is roughly 2,000 times sweeter than sucrose. The molecule decomposes under certain conditions to derivatives of its component parts, which are discussed in more detail in Chapter 2.

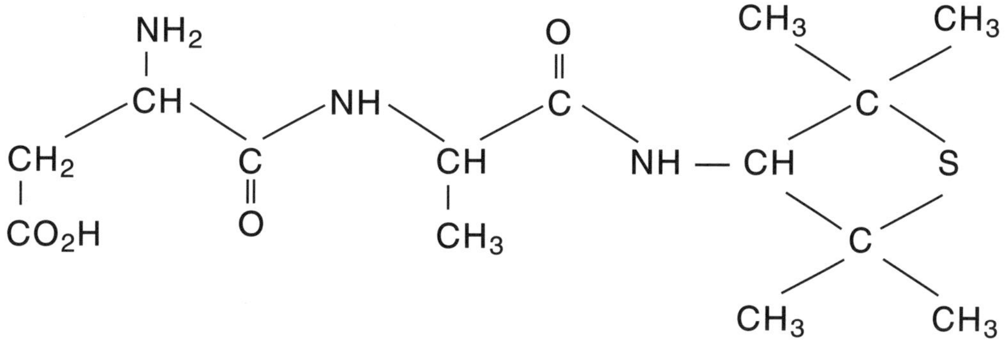

**Fig. 1-4.** Chemical structure of alitame.

**Legal status.** Alitame has been approved for use in countries such as Australia, New Zealand, Mexico, and China. Petitions for approval have been filed in many other countries including the United Kingdom, the Netherlands, France, and Canada. In the United States, the petition for food additive status was filed in 1986 and is still under review.

## ACESULFAME POTASSIUM

**History.** In 1967, while reacting butyne and fluorosulfonyl isocyanate in a research laboratory at the Hoechst Company in Germany, Karl Clauss accidentally noticed a sweet taste on his fingers (7). A research effort was launched to investigate this class of compounds known as dihydrooxathiazinone dioxides. A derivative was found that was very sweet and exhibited a very clean taste. This compound is now known as acesulfame potassium or acesulfame K. The sweetener is known in the food industry by its brand name, Sunett. Because of its bitter taste, it is commonly used in a blend with other high-intensity sweeteners.

**Description.** Acesulfame K is a white, crystalline powder that is about 200 times sweeter than sucrose. Its chemical structure is shown in Figure 1-5. The molecule is stable and is not known to decompose with digestion and therefore is excreted unchanged.

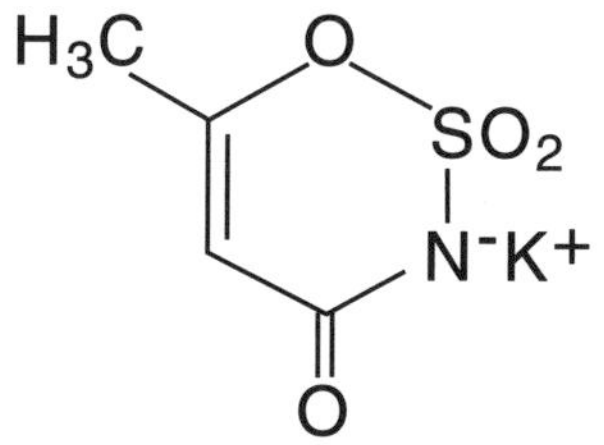

**Legal status.** Acesulfame K is approved for use in more than 25 countries. More than 90 in-depth safety studies have shown that acesulfame K is not mutagenic or carcinogenic. It was first approved in England in 1983. In 1988, it was approved in the United States for use in several applications, including chewing gum, dry mix beverages, instant coffees and teas, gelatins, puddings, nondairy creamers, and tabletop sweeteners. In 1998, it was approved for use in soft drinks.

**Fig. 1-5.** Chemical structure of acesulfame K.

## SUCRALOSE

**History.** During the 1970s, the British firm Tate & Lyle, in association with carbohydrate chemistry researchers at the Queen Elizabeth

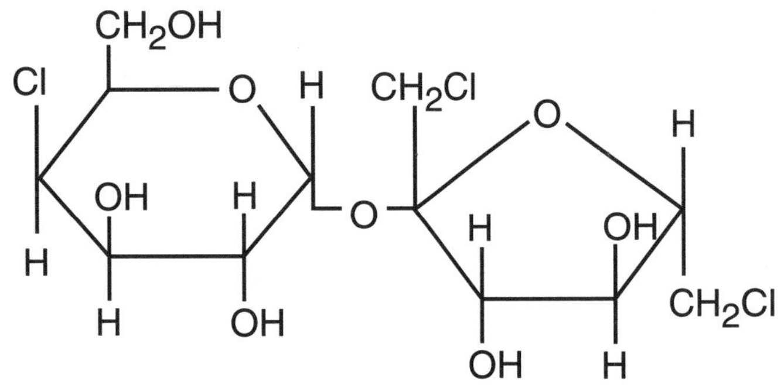

**Fig. 1-6.** Chemical structure of sucralose.

College in London, set about to create new entities from sucrose. In 1976, the team developed sucralose (8). The process by which it is produced is patented and involves replacing three hydroxyl groups on the sucrose molecule with three chlorine atoms. Sucralose, known by the brand name Splenda, is the only high-intensity synthetic sweetener currently made from sucrose. It is jointly marketed by the McNeil Specialty Products Company of the United States and Tate & Lyle.

**Description.** Sucralose is made directly from the sucrose molecule. It is selectively halogenated with chlorine, which replaces three hydroxyl groups. The structure of sucralose is shown in Figure 1-6. It is roughly 400–800 times sweeter than sucrose.

**Legal status.** Sucralose has been the subject of more than 100 animal and human studies, and results have shown that it is safe for consumption and is not carcinogenic or mutagenic. It is not metabolized when ingested and is mostly excreted in the feces unchanged from its original form. Sucralose is currently approved for use in more than 30 countries. It was approved in the United States in 1999 as a general-purpose sweetener and can be used in all food and beverage applications and in nutritional supplements, medical foods, and vitamin and mineral supplements.

# Naturally Occurring High-Intensity Sweeteners

The history, structure, and legal status of the most common natural high-intensity sweeteners are discussed here. Details about some of those that are less common are summarized in Table 1-2.

**TABLE 1-2.** Less Common Natural High-Intensity Sweeteners

| Sweetener | Sweetness Intensity (sucrose = 1) | Chemical Nature | Comments |
|---|---|---|---|
| Dihydrochalcones | 300–2,000 | Flavonoid | Produced from naringin, a compound in grapefruit peels. Not widely used. |
| Hernandulcin | 1,000–1,200 | Sesquiterpene | Isolated from the herb *Lippia dulcis*. Very bitter tasting. |
| Monellin | 1,500–2,000 | Protein | From the fruit of an African plant. Strong, lingering aftertaste. Costly to produce; hard to grow. |

## THAUMATINS

**History.** In 1855, the fruit of *Thaumatococcus daniellii,* a plant found in West Africa, Uganda, and Sudan, was noted to have a very sweet taste. In 1979, two proteins, thaumatin I and thaumatin II, were characterized as the cause of the sweet taste (1–3). The British firm Tate & Lyle markets the proteins as Talin.

**Description.** Thaumatin I and thaumatin II are very similar in nature. Both are very large protein molecules. Their amino acids have each been sequenced, and their molecular weights are 22,209 and 22,293, respectively. They are about 2,000–3,000 times sweeter than sucrose.

**Legal status.** Thaumatins were approved for use in Japan in 1979. They are currently approved in Australia and the United Kingdom and are awaiting regulatory approval in several other countries. However, the applications for approval suggest that thaumatins are more suitable for use as flavor enhancers than as high-intensity sweeteners. In fact, thaumatins have been granted GRAS status in the United States as flavor enhancers but not as sweeteners.

| Sweetness Intensity of Common High-Intensity Sweeteners Compared with That of Sucrose | |
|---|---|
| Sweetener | Times Sweeter Than Sucrose |
| Synthetic | |
| Saccharin | 300–600 |
| Cyclamate | 30 |
| Aspartame | 160–220 |
| Alitame | 2,000 |
| Acesulfame K | 200 |
| Sucralose | 400–800 |
| Natural | |
| Thaumatin | 2,000–3,000 |
| Glycyrrhizin | 50–100 |
| Stevioside | 200–300 |

## GLYCYRRHIZIN

**History.** First isolated in 1970, glycyrrhizin is a compound that is extracted from the roots of the licorice plant, *Glycyrrhiza* (1–3). Licorice has been known as a healing herb and medicinal plant since ancient times. Its healing properties are being explored even today in areas such as AIDS research and studies of immunological function. Ammoniated glycyrrhizin, a form that is readily water soluble, is used most often in food applications.

**Description.** Glycyrrhizin is a *triterpenoid* (Fig. 1-7). It is approximately 50–100 times sweeter than sucrose (ammoniated glycyrrhizin is approximately 50 times sweeter than sucrose) and has a notably long aftertaste.

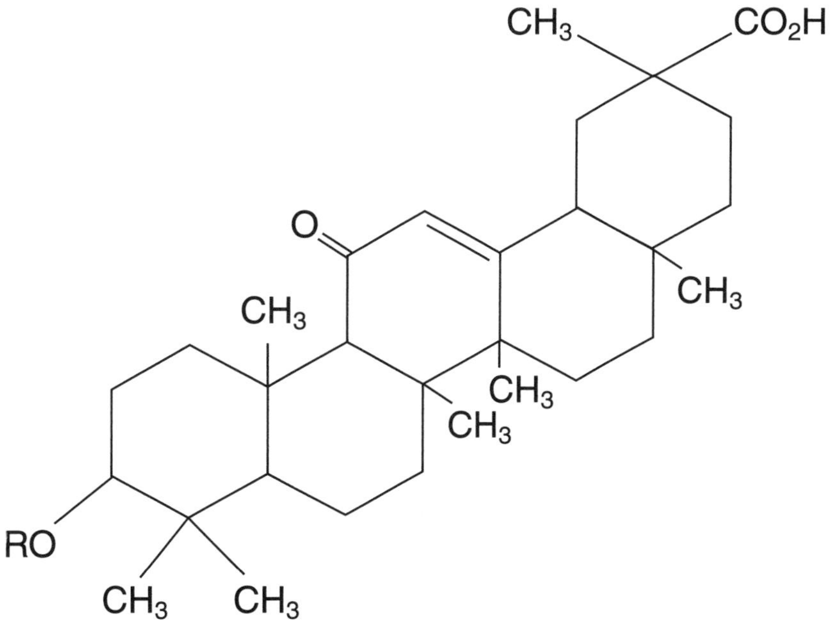

**Fig. 1-7.** Chemical structure of glycyrrhizin. R = β-GlcCO$_2$H – β-GlcCO$_2$H(2←1), in which Glc = glucuronopyranosyl.

**Legal status.** In Japan, glycyrrhizin is widely used as a sweetening agent in many food and beverage applications. It is also used in many countries for its medicinal properties as well as in food

**Triterpenoid**—A terpene with three isoprene units in its structure.

applications. Ammoniated glycyrrhizin is on the GRAS list of food additives for natural flavoring agents in the United States, but it is not approved as a sweetening agent. Ingestion of large amounts of glycyrrhizin has resulted in edema, headaches, hypertension, and fatigue. The Ministry of Health in Japan has cautioned that usage levels should not exceed 100 mg per day in drug formulations (1).

## STEVIOSIDE

**History.** The leaves of the South American stevia plant have been used for centuries to sweeten bitter medicines and teas. It was encountered by the Spanish conquistadors in South America during the sixteenth century. In 1899, the plant was described by M. S. Bertoni and given the botanical name *Stevia rebaudiana* Bertoni (9).

One of the compounds responsible for the sweetness is stevioside, which was first concentrated from the leaves of the stevia plant during the early 1900s. It was isolated in a pure form during the 1970s in Japan, where it was used as a sweetening agent. Eight compounds have now been found to contribute to the sweetness of the stevia leaves. Stevioside is the most popular and the most utilized of these eight isolated forms. Stevia is currently cultivated in Japan, Korea, and China.

**Description.** Stevioside is a *diterpenoid* compound. The structure is shown in Figure 1-8. The leaves from the stevia plant are about 30 times sweeter than sucrose, and purified stevioside is 200–300 times sweeter than sugar. It is known for its sweet intensity, slight bitterness, and slight licorice flavor in the powder form. Once it is dissolved in liquid, the bitterness and licorice notes are less apparent.

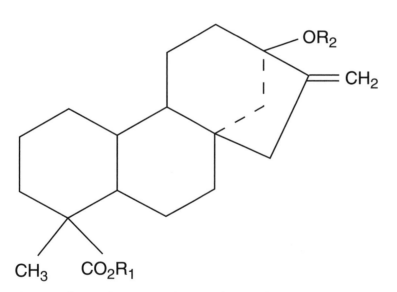

**Fig. 1-8.** Chemical structure of stevioside. $R_1$ = β-glucopyranosyl, and $R_2$ = β-glucopyranosyl² – β-glucopyranosyl.

**Diterpenoid**—A terpene with two isoprene units in its structure.

**Glucose**—A six-carbon simple sugar.

**Legal status.** Stevioside is widely used in Japan as a sweetening agent and flavor enhancer. It is also used in many other countries including Israel, Brazil, China, Taiwan, Paraguay, and Korea. Many studies have shown stevia and stevioside to be safe. Stevia leaves have been used for their proposed medicinal properties, which include combating fatigue, facilitating digestion, regulating blood *glucose* levels, sustaining feelings of vitality and well-being, and caring for the skin. Stevia is not an approved food additive in the United States and does not have GRAS status. In 1991, Congress passed the Dietary Supplement Act, which allowed the use of stevioside as a dietary supplement or a dietary supplement ingredient but not as a food additive (i.e., sweetener). In countries other than the United States, its is used in products such as tabletop sweeteners, soft drinks, juices, confectionery, jams, yogurts, baked goods, and chewing gum.

## Sugar Alcohols

Although they do not exhibit high sweetness intensity, sugar alcohols represent a category of sweeteners that provide the product developer with several different types of food-development options. They can be used in sugar-free foods, reduced-calorie foods, and foods

---

**Box 1.2. New Sweeteners**

**Neotame.** Neotame is a relatively new synthetic high-intensity sweetener developed by Monsanto. In December 1997, a petition was filed with the FDA for approval of its use as a tabletop sweetener, and in April 1999, another petition was filed for general-use approval. It is currently not used in countries other than the United States. Neotame is similar to aspartame, also developed by Monsanto. It is composed of the same two amino acids, L-aspartate and L-phenylalanine, and has two functional groups, a methyl ester group and a neohexyl group. Neotame is approximately 8,000 times sweeter than sucrose and about 40 times sweeter than aspartame. It has a clean, sweet taste with some flavor-enhancement properties and withstands baking and cooking temperatures. Neotame is quickly metabolized and completely eliminated by the body and contributes zero calories at the level of use in foods.

**Tagatose.** Tagatose is a low-calorie bulk sweetener derived from lactose. MD Food Ingredients filed a petition with the FDA for GRAS status in October 1998. It is 92% as sweet as sucrose and has only 1.5 calories per gram. It also has flavor-enhancing properties when used in soft drink applications. It is noncariogenic and does not cause a rise in blood glucose levels. Tagatose also exhibits a prebiotic effect. When it is digested, butyrate production increases in the colon, which increases the number of lactobacilli there. Therefore, tagatose is considered a sweetening agent for both food and functional food applications.

**Erythritol.** Erythritol is a fairly new sugar alcohol available to the food industry. It occurs naturally in melons, mushrooms, pears, and grapes and has been commercially produced by a fermentation process since 1990. It has also been used in products in Japan since 1990. In January 1997, the FDA accepted the GRAS petition. Erythritol is 70% as sweet as sucrose and has a clean, sweet taste with no aftertaste. It is nonhygroscopic and noncariogenic and has a nonlaxative effect. It does not cause a rise in blood glucose levels. Its caloric value for food labeling is 0.2 calories per gram in the United States and zero calories per gram in Japan.

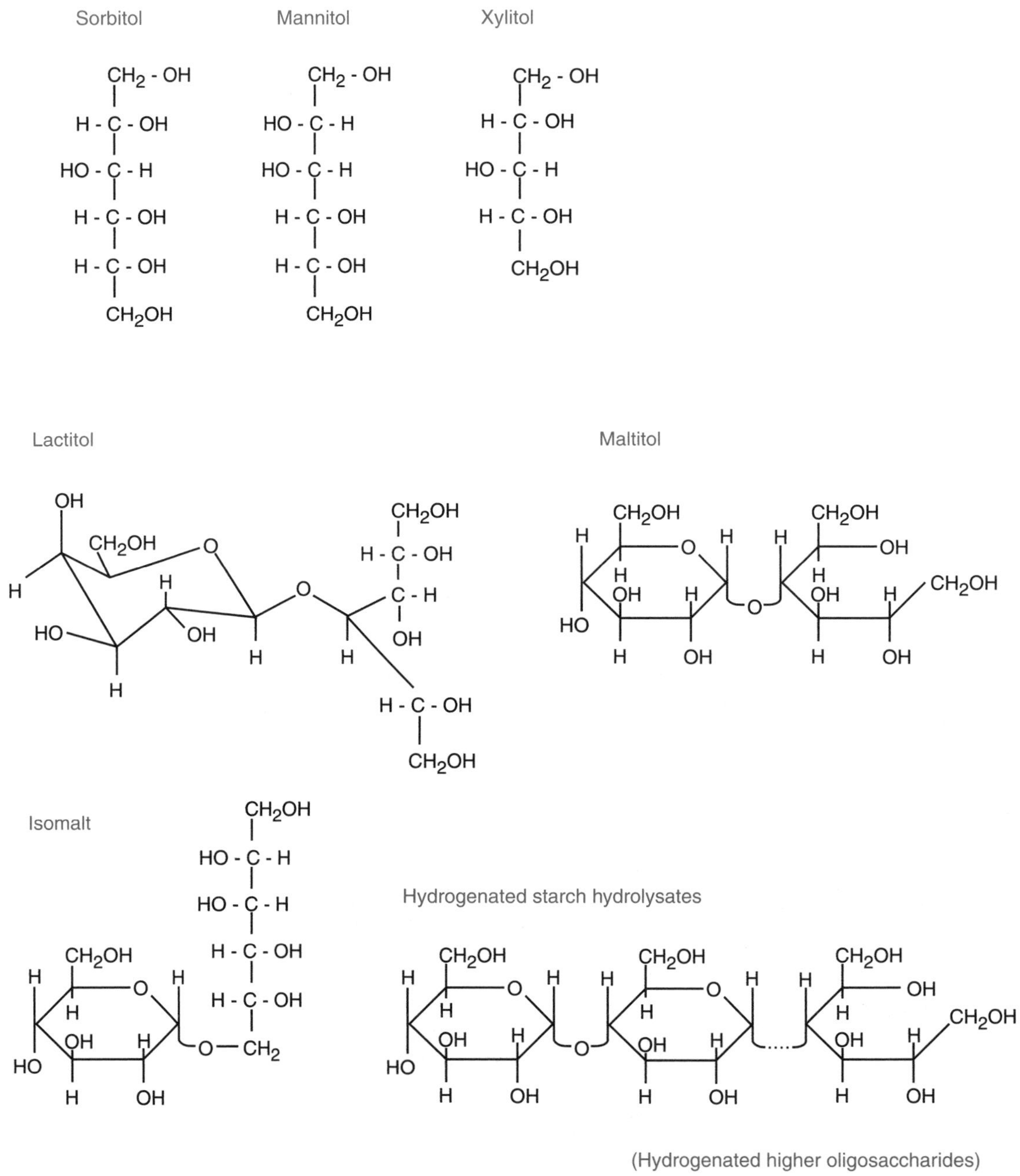

Sorbitol   Mannitol   Xylitol

Lactitol                                Maltitol

Isomalt

Hydrogenated starch hydrolysates

(Hydrogenated higher oligosaccharides)

**Fig. 1-9.** Chemical structures of the sugar alcohols sorbitol, mannitol, xylitol, lactitol, maltitol, isomalt, and hydrogenated starch hydrolysates.

**Cariogenic**—Capable of causing tooth decay (caries).

**Polyol**—Sugar alcohol, a compound derived from the reduction of sugar.

that are *noncariogenic*. Sugar alcohols are also referred to as *polyols*. Those commonly used in foods include sorbitol, mannitol, xylitol, lactitol, maltitol, isomalt, and hydrogenated starch hydrolysates (a mixture of sugar alcohols). The structures of these sugar alcohols are shown in Figure 1-9.

**History.** Some sugar alcohols have been known since the beginning of the century, while others have been more recently developed. Chemist Joseph Boussingault, for example, found sorbitol as early as 1872 and isolated the compound from the berries of the mountain ash tree (1). It was also found to occur naturally in several fruits and berries and as a human metabolite. Mannitol was found in the exudate of an ash tree. Xylitol was discovered in 1891 by a German chemist named Emil Fischer. It also occurs naturally in several fruits and vegetables and is a human metabolite. Lactitol was discovered during the 1920s and developed for production during the 1930s; further development occurred during the 1980s. During the 1960s, maltitol was developed in Japan, hydrogenated starch hydrolysates in Sweden, and isomalt in Europe.

**Ketose**—A sugar molecule containing the ketone group at the carbon molecule adjacent to the terminal carbon.

**Fructose**—A six-carbon keto sugar naturally present in fruits and honey and produced by the isomerization of glucose.

**Hexose**—A six-carbon simple sugar molecule (e.g., glucose).

**Description.** A sugar alcohol, or polyol, can be defined as the reduction product of a sugar molecule. The carbonyl group of a *ketose* sugar (e.g., *fructose*) or *hexose* sugar (e.g., glucose) is reduced to a hydroxyl group (i.e., an alcohol group). The reduction of a single simple sugar molecule may result in two different sugar alcohol end products, since the reducing group (an aldehyde or ketone group) may be located at an asymmetric carbon. For example, the reduction of fructose can yield both sorbitol and mannitol. In addition, the reduction of two different simple sugar molecules can yield the same sugar alcohol end product because their reducing groups are at the same molecular location. The reduction of either glucose or fructose, for example, yields sorbitol (Fig. 1-10).

While many sugar alcohols are found in nature, it is not commercially fea-

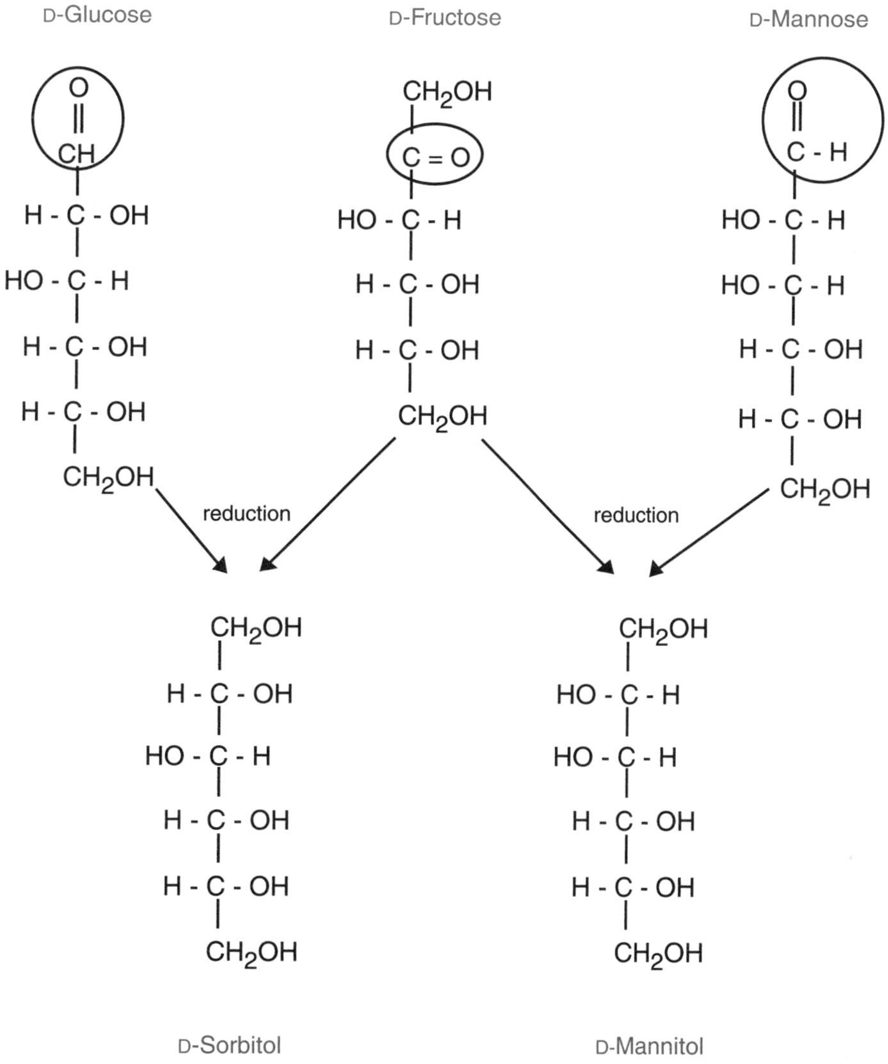

**Fig. 1-10.** Reduction of glucose, fructose, and mannose. Reduced groups are circled.

**Polysaccharide**—A carbon containing several hundred, thousand, or hundred thousand sugar units (from the Greek *poly*, meaning "many").

**Xylose**—A five-carbon aldo sugar derived from xylan hemicellulose, a by-product of paper pulp manufacture.

sible to isolate and concentrate them from their sources. Sorbitol, mannitol, maltitol, and the hydrogenated starch hydrolysates are produced by the procedure outlined in Figure 1-11. In general, the process of producing these sugar alcohols begins with the enzymatic hydrolysis of a starch. Corn, wheat, or potato starch can all be used. The enzyme(s) used and the hydrolysis time determine which sugar alcohol(s) is produced. The hydrolyzed product then undergoes catalytic hydrogenation, producing a syrup of the sugar alcohol(s). The syrup is further purified, and depending upon the sugar alcohol end product, a crystalline product, syrup, or both may result.

Lactitol, xylitol, and isomalt are produced in roughly the same manner (i.e., hydrogenation or reduction), except that they are not derived from starch. Lactose, the sugar isolated from milk, is catalytically hydrogenated (i.e., reduced) to lactitol. Xylitol is derived from xylan, a complex *polysaccharide* found in birchwood, almond shells, straw, and corncobs. It is also a secondary stream by-product in the paper-making industry. Xylan is chemically converted to the simple sugar *xylose*, which is then catalytically hydrogenated to xylitol. Isomalt is produced in a two-step process. First, an enzyme rearranges the fructose and glucose chemical bond of the sucrose molecule. Next, the fructose portion of the rearranged sucrose molecule undergoes catalytic hydrogenation. During this reduction step, roughly half the fructose portion is converted to mannitol and half is converted to sorbitol. This is common for the reduction of the fructose

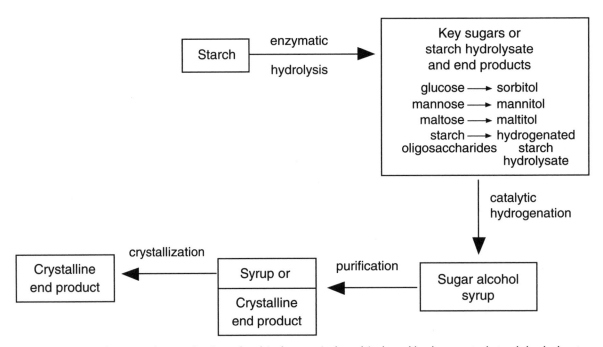

Fig. 1-11. General process for production of sorbitol, mannitol, maltitol, and hydrogenated starch hydrolysates.

**TABLE 1-3.** Characteristics of Sugar Alcohols

| Sugar Alcohol | Number of Countries Approved in and/or Listing | U.S. Allowed Caloric Value (calories/g) | Sweetness Intensity (sucrose = 1) |
|---|---|---|---|
| Sorbitol | Numerous; GRAS in U.S. | 2.6 | 0.5–0.7 |
| Mannitol | Numerous; GRAS in U.S. | 1.6 | 0.5–0.7 |
| Xylitol | >35 (includes U.S.) | 2.4 | 1 |
| Lactitol | Several, including U.S., Canada, Japan, Israel, Switzerland | 2.0 | 0.3–0.4 |
| Maltitol | >10 (includes U.S.) | 2.1 | 0.9 |
| Isomalt (Palatinit) | >40 (includes U.S.) | 2.0 | 0.45–0.65 |
| Hydrogenated starch hydrolysates | >10, including Canada, Japan, Australia, & U.S. | 3.0 | 0.25–0.75 |

molecule as described earlier (Fig. 1-10), and the final products are two *disaccharide* alcohols, a gluco-mannitol and a gluco-sorbitol (Fig. 1-9).

A more detailed discussion of the characteristics of sugar alcohols is provided in Chapter 3.

**Legal status.** Sugar alcohols have been used for many years in foods in many countries, and their safety has been studied and proved. The acceptable daily intakes for sugar alcohols have been established as "not specified," which is the safest category status that a food additive can obtain. The caloric values have been determined for many sugar alcohols, and the FDA allows use of these values for determining the caloric value declared on food labels. The legal status and allowed caloric values for the major sugar alcohols are given in Table 1-3.

## References

1. O'Brien Nabors, L., and Gelardi, R. C., Eds. 1991. *Alternative Sweeteners,* 2nd ed. Marcel Dekker, New York.
2. Krutosikova, A., and Uher, M. 1992. *Natural and Synthetic Sweet Substances.* Ellis Horwood, New York.
3. Marie, S., and Piggott, J. R. 1991. *Handbook of Sweeteners.* AVI, New York.
4. Whelan, E. M., and Stare, F. J. 1977. Food additives in relation to health—A challenge to those responsible for nutrition education. Alimentaria 83:23, 25-27.
5. Audrieth, L. F., and Sveda, M. 1944. Preparation and properties of some *N*-substituted sulfamic acids. J. Org. Chem. 9:89-101.
6. Brennan, T. M., and Hendrick, M. E. 1983. U.S. patent 4,411,925.
7. Mayer, D. G., and Kemper, F. H., Eds. 1991. *Acesulfame-K.* Marcel Dekker, New York.
8. Jenner, M. R., and Smithson, A. 1989. Physico-chemical properties of the sweetener sucralose. J. Food Sci. 54:1646-1649.
9. The JAJA Group, Inc. 1998. Stevia history. On-line information.

**Disaccharide**—A carbohydrate containing two sugar units, each composed of five or six carbon atoms in a furanose or pyranose ring.

# Properties of High-Intensity Sweeteners

High-intensity sweeteners are agents that exhibit sweetening powers at very low concentrations. This sweetening power is most often compared with that of sucrose and is called the *relative sweetness*. For example, the compound aspartame is about 160–220 times sweeter than sucrose and is considered a high-intensity, or high-potency, sweetener. These sweeteners are useful in the development of low-calorie foods because although they may be caloric, they are used only at very low levels in the final products. They are also often used in the development of foods to help prevent dental caries and in foods eaten by diabetics because they do not promote dental caries or raise blood sugar levels. The high-intensity sweeteners discussed here are those commonly used in the food industry worldwide and are either synthetic or naturally occurring. The synthetic sweeteners are saccharin, cyclamate, aspartame, alitame, acesulfame K, and sucralose. The naturally occurring sweeteners are thaumatin, stevioside, and glycyrrhizin.

It is important to understand the physical and chemical properties of the high-intensity sweeteners, since they can be very different from the properties of the sucrose or other nutritive sweeteners they are replacing in a food system. *Sweeteners: Nutritive* (1) reviews the properties of sucrose and other natural or carbohydrate-based sweeteners such as corn syrups, honey, and dextrose. An understanding of a particular high-intensity sweetener's properties, such as sweetening ability, solubility, and stability at various pH levels and temperatures, and how to analytically determine its presence is crucial during the product-development and processing stages.

| In This Chapter: |
| :--- |
| **General Comparisons** |
| Sweetness and Solubility |
| Physical and Chemical Characteristics |
| **Synthetic High-Intensity Sweeteners** |
| Saccharin |
| Cyclamates |
| Aspartame |
| Alitame |
| Acesulfame Potassium |
| Sucralose |
| **Naturally Occurring High-Intensity Sweeteners** |
| Thaumatin |
| Stevioside |
| Glycyrrhizin |

## General Comparisons

### SWEETNESS AND SOLUBILITY

Each high-intensity sweetener has its own characteristics. The range of its sweetening ability depends on the sweetener's relative sweetness and its ability to be incorporated into a particular system. Therefore, comparing the solubilities of various alternative sweeteners can be helpful in selecting one for a specific application. The relative sweetness, solubility, and aqueous stability of synthetic high-intensity sweeteners are compared in Table 2-1. Temporal sweetness is compared in Table 2-2. All the sweeteners have a sweetness duration longer than that of sucrose, and most reach maximum intensity

**Relative sweetness—**
Sweetness of a substance compared with that of a reference substance (usually sucrose).

**TABLE 2-1.** Comparison of Synthetic High-Intensity Sweeteners[a]

| Sweetener | Approximate Sweetness (sucrose = 1) | Solubility in Water | Aqueous Stability |
|---|---|---|---|
| Acesulfame K | 200 | Excellent | Excellent |
| Alitame | 2,000 | Excellent | Fair to good |
| Aspartame | 160–220 | Good | Fair |
| Cyclamates | 30 | Excellent | Excellent |
| Saccharin | 300–600 | Excellent | Excellent |
| Sucralose | 400–800 | Excellent | Excellent |

[a] Courtesy R. Deis.

**TABLE 2-2.** Temporal Profiles of High-Intensity Sweeteners[a, b]

| Sweetener | Time to Maximum Intensity (sec) | Extinction Time[c] (sec) | Sweetness Duration (sec) |
|---|---|---|---|
| Sucrose | 4.1 | 14 | 66.1 |
| Sodium saccharin | 3.1 | 14 | 77.2 |
| Sodium cyclamate | 4.0 | 14 | . . . |
| Sucralose | 5.0 | . . . | 75.4 |
| Aspartame | 6.2 | 19 | 76.7 |
| Acesulfame K | 4.9 | . . . | 77.4 |

[a] Courtesy J. Bell.

[b] Temporal properties may differ as a result of sweetener concentration and other formulation issues.

[c] Time from maximum intensity to end of response.

**TABLE 2-3.** Relative Potency of High-Intensity Sweeteners[a]

| Sweetener | Reported Potency | Potency at Sucrose Level 2% | 8% | 10% |
|---|---|---|---|---|
| Sucrose | 1.0 | 1.0 | 1.0 | 1.0 |
| Acesulfame K | 200 | 204 | 77 | 34 |
| Alitame | 2,000 | 4,500 | 2,355 | 1,640 |
| Aspartame | 200 | 250 | 143 | 107 |
| Sodium cyclamate | 30 | 26 | 27 | 18 |
| Sodium saccharin | 300 | 510 | 188 | . . . |
| Sucralose | 600 | 614 | 520 | 385 |

[a] Courtesy R. Deis.

**Maillard browning—**
Nonenzymatic, heat-induced browning of foods that occurs over time.

more slowly. The relative potency information in Table 2-3 can be used as an indication of sweetness. However, potency often is not a linear function, and the individual system should be considered because masking or enhancement effects can occur. It should also be noted that the potency of the high-intensity sweeteners listed decreases as concentration increases. Information on solubility, sweetness, and other properties is discussed in more detail in the sections on specific sweeteners.

## PHYSICAL AND CHEMICAL CHARACTERISTICS

Nutritive sweeteners such as sucrose, dextrose, and corn syrups contribute to many of the physical characteristics of food. For example, they influence viscosity, texture, and bulk. Since high-intensity sweeteners achieve the desired sweetening effect at such low concentrations, most often they do not contribute to these characteristics.

Nutritive sweeteners also affect microbial activity and some of the chemical reactions of foods, such as *Maillard browning*. Saccharin, cyclamate, acesulfame K, sucralose, glycyrrhizin, and stevioside do not undergo Maillard browning, a reaction that occurs between a *reducing sugar* (one that has a reactive carbonyl group) and an amine group. Simple reducing sugars such as glucose and fructose readily participate in this reaction to cause browning in sweetened foods such as cookies and caramels. Because it is a nonreducing sugar, sucrose does not participate in the reaction. However, its component sugars, glucose and fructose, do. Therefore, when sucrose hydrolyzes (at low pH or high temperatures), it participates in the reaction. Although protein-based high-intensity sweeteners such as aspartame, alitame, and thaumatin contain amine groups that can participate in the reaction, they rarely cause such browning to occur because of their low concentration in food systems. However, their participation in the reaction can cause a decrease in the sweetening effect or a loss of sweetness.

Nutritive sweeteners used in high concentrations lower the water activity of a food system, thereby restricting the growth of microbes and retarding spoilage. Because of their chemical nature and low concentrations in formulated foods, high-intensity sweeteners do not lower the water activity, and thus their use may allow microbial spoilage.

In the development of new products in which high-intensity sweeteners are substituted for nutritive sweeteners, efforts are focused on maintaining the physical and chemical characteristics of the foods. This topic is discussed further in the application chapters.

**Reducing sugar**—A sugar molecule in which the carbonyl group can react to form a carboxylic acid group. The sugar can undergo nonenzymatic (Maillard) browning.

# Synthetic High-Intensity Sweeteners

## SACCHARIN

Saccharin is available as acid saccharin, calcium saccharin, and the sodium salt form. All three products are white, crystalline powders that are extremely stable in their dry state. The properties of each saccharin form are shown in Table 2-4. Saccharin is known to have a bitter, metallic aftertaste, which can be masked by blending it with other sweeteners such as cyclamates, aspartame, acesulfame K, or sucralose. The aftertaste of calcium saccharin is cleaner and less bitter than that of the other saccharin forms.

**Solubility.** The solubility of the three forms of saccharin in water at various temperatures is shown in Table 2-4. Saccharin is also soluble in acetone, ethanol, and glycerol and is slightly soluble in chloroform and diethyl ether.

**TABLE 2-4.** Properties of Saccharin Forms[a]

|  | Acid Saccharin | Sodium Saccharin | Calcium Saccharin |
|---|---|---|---|
| Molecular formula | $C_7H_5NO_3S$ | $C_7H_4NO_3SNa\cdot2H_2O$ | $[C_7H_4NO_3S]_2Ca\cdot2H_2O$ |
| Molecular weight | 183.18 | 241.20 | 440.48 |
| CAS[b] Registry no. | 81-07-2 | 128-44-9 | 6485-34-3 |
| Melting point (°C) | 228–229 | >300 | >300 |
| Appearance | White solid | White solid | White solid |
| $pK_a$[c] | 1.30 | . . . | . . . |
| Solubility (g/100 g of water) at |  |  |  |
| 20°C | 0.2 | 100 | 37 |
| 35°C | 0.4 | 143 | 82 |
| 50°C | 0.7 | 187 | 127 |
| 75°C | 1.3 | 254 | 202 |
| 90°C | . . . | 297 | 247 |

[a] Reprinted, with permission, from (5).
[b] Chemical Abstract Service.
[c] Dissociation constant, i.e., the pH at which the hydrogen ion dissociates.

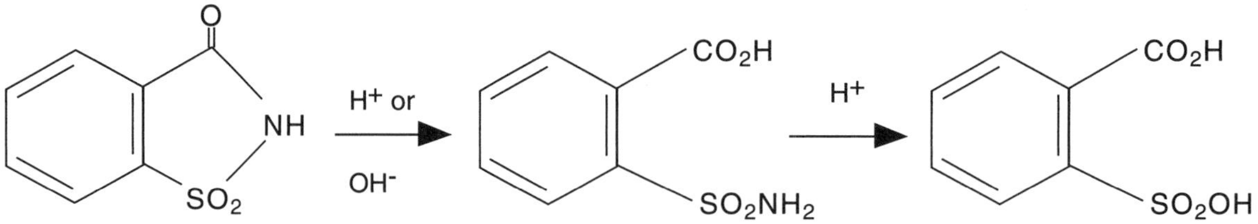


Saccharin 2-Sulfobenzoic acid 2-Sulfamoylbenzoic acid

**Fig. 2-1.** Hydrolytic decomposition of saccharin at pH <2 and very high temperature.

**Stability.** At pH <2.0 and at extremely high temperatures, hydrolytic decomposition to 2-sulfobenzoic acid and 2-sulfamoylbenzoic acid can occur (Fig. 2-1). Neither of these compounds exhibits sweetness. Saccharin is stable when heated at normal food-processing temperatures, but when heated to decomposition (380°C), all three saccharin forms emit toxic fumes of nitrogen oxides and sulfur oxides. Although saccharin does not decompose under the conditions encountered during typical food processing, some hydrolysis occurs after prolonged exposure to extreme conditions of temperature or pH.

Figure 2-2 shows the hydrolysis curves for the decomposition of saccharin at various pH levels and temperatures.

**Analytical determinations.** The presence of saccharin in foods and beverages can be determined by a combination of thin-layer chromatography, extraction, and UV spectrophotometry. High-performance liquid chromatography (HPLC) and ion-pair chromatography (2) and titration with Sudan Blue GN and Sudan Green 4B indicators can also be used.

## CYCLAMATES

The three forms, cyclamic acid (cyclamate), sodium cyclamate, and calcium cyclamate, are all white, crystalline powders. Sodium cyclamate and calcium cyclamate can also be produced as white crystals. Cyclamates have a pleasant taste profile and are good alternative sweeteners for masking bitter notes. Calcium cyclamate is slightly less sweet than the other two forms. Cyclamates can be combined with saccharin (the most common ratio is 10 parts cyclamate to 1 part saccharin by weight [3]) in a synergistic blend to decrease the perceived bitterness of saccharin. Cyclamates are used to enhance fruit flavors. It is now banned in the United States.

**Solubility.** Cyclamates are easily dissolved in aqueous solutions and yield a clear solution. They are very stable at the pH levels encountered during processing. Cyclamic acid is soluble in water at 1 g/13 ml (4) and in ethanol, glycerol, ethyl acetate, and acetone. A 10% aqueous solution has a pH of 0.8–1.6. Sodium cyclamate is soluble in water at 1 g/5 ml (4) but only slightly soluble in ethanol, benzene, chloroform, acetone, and ether. Calcium cyclamate is soluble in water at 1 g/4 ml (4) and is slightly soluble in ethanol. It is insoluble in benzene, chloroform, and ether.

**Stability.** Sodium and calcium cyclamate decompose at 260°C. Cyclamic acid has a melting point of 169–170°C. They are stable at baking temperatures and during heating in solutions. They have a long shelf life in their dry state and are not *hygroscopic*. Cyclohexamine, a metabolic breakdown product, is produced from the microflora of the intestine (5) but is not produced during the processing of food systems.

**Analytical determinations.** Cyclamates can be analyzed by using gas chromatography with a UV absorption detector at 315 nm (4). For isolation and determination in food systems, a method employing extraction, thin-layer chromatography, and UV spectroscopy can be used (4). HPLC, high-performance ion chromatography, and titrametric methods are also commonly used in the determination of cyclamates in foods (4).

## ASPARTAME

Aspartame is a white, crystalline, odorless compound. It is a dipeptide of phenylalanine and aspartate and also contains a methyl ester. Aspartame is a clean-tasting, synthetic sweetener that leaves no bitter or metallic aftertaste, although, like most high-intensity sweeteners, it can leave a lingering sweet taste. Aspartame enhances fruit flavors and works well in acid-type, fruit-based systems, most noticeably those that contain natural fruit. In its dry state, aspartame decomposes at temperatures >150°C and has a melting point of 246–247°C.

**Solubility.** Aspartame is slightly soluble in water. Because of its polar nature, it is not soluble in fats and oils. In solution at room temperature, the maximum solubility is reached at pH 2.2. Because it is a dipeptide, it is *amphoteric,* and those sites can dissociate hydrogen

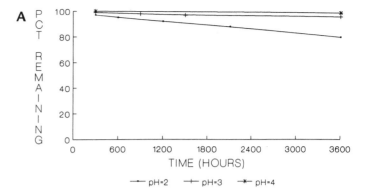

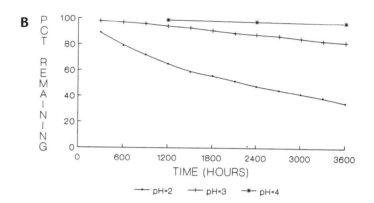

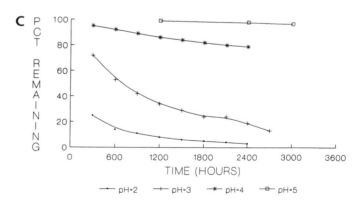

**Fig. 2-2.** Effects of temperature on saccharin hydrolysis. **A,** 20°C (68°F); **B,** 40°C (104°F); **C,** 80°C (176°F). (Reprinted, with permission, from M. L. Mitchell and R. L. Pearson, Saccharin, pages 127-156 in: [5])

**Hygroscopicity**—Ability to attract and retain moisture.

**Amphoteric**—Pertaining to a compound that has both positive and negative charges.

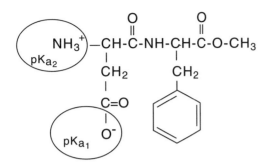

**Fig. 2-3.** Dissociation constants (pKas) of aspartame. pK$_{a_1}$ = 3.1; pK$_{a_2}$ = 7.9. Dissociation sites are circled.

**A**

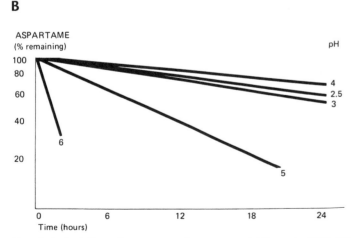

**B**

**Fig. 2-4.** Stability of aspartame in aqueous buffers at 40°C (**A**) and 80°C (**B**) at various pH levels. (Reprinted, with permission, from B. E. Homler, R. C. Deis, and W. H. Shazer, Aspartame, pages 39-69 in: [5])

ions (Fig. 2-3). The dissociation constant is also called pK$_a$, which is defined as the pH at which the hydrogen ion dissociates. The pK$_a$s of the two sites are 3.1 and 7.9 at 25°C. The molecule still exhibits sweetness after the sites are dissociated. The *isoelectric point* is also important because it defines the pH at which the molecule exhibits no charge and can therefore settle out of a solution. The isoelectric point for aspartame is 5.2.

**Stability.** Aspartame is very stable in its dry state. Its stability in solution is very much a function of pH and temperature. In general, aspartame is stable at pH 3–5. It is most stable at pH 4.3. It is less stable at pH >5 and also becomes less stable with heat. The stability of aspartame in aqueous buffered solutions at 40 and 80°C is shown in Figure 2-4.

Because of its dipeptide nature, aspartame is subject to hydrolysis and use by microbes. It can also participate in chemical reactions such as Maillard browning. In aqueous solutions at certain temperatures and pH levels, aspartame hydrolyzes, forming the end products methanol and the dipeptide aspartylphenylalanine (Fig. 2-5). These end products exhibit no sweetness. In addition, in its dry state or under aqueous conditions, aspartame can *cyclize* to form the compound diketopiperazine (DKP). This reaction is most prominent at neutral and basic pH levels with heat. The effects of temperature on the decomposition of dry aspartame to DKP are shown in Figure 2-6. Once this reaction occurs, the sweetness is lost. DKP decreases the sweetness of aspartame, even if the reaction is not complete and aspartame is still present. If aspartame decomposes and forms methanol and aspartylphenylalanine, the dipeptide can also cyclize to form DKP.

**Analytical determinations.** Pure aspartame can be readily determined fluorometrically (4). In aqueous food systems such as beverages, thin-layer chromatography can be employed. For complex food systems, extraction followed by HPLC is used. The decomposition products can also be determined by this analytical procedure.

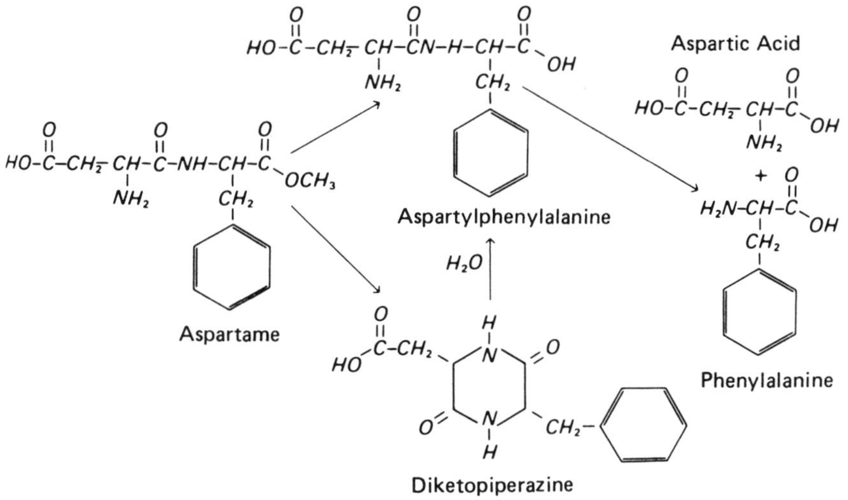

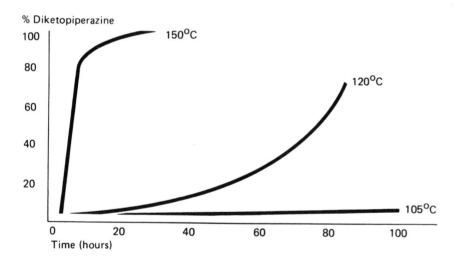

**Fig. 2-5.** Reaction pathways by which aspartame can undergo breakdown. (Courtesy NutraSweet Group)

% Diketopiperazine

**Fig. 2-6.** Rate of decomposition of dry aspartame to diketopiperazine at 150, 120, and 105°C. (Reprinted, with permission, from B. E. Homler, R. C. Deis, and W. H. Shazer, Aspartame, pages 39-69 in: [5])

## ALITAME

Alitame, like aspartame, is a dipeptide sweetener containing the amino acids aspartate and alanine and an amide group. It is a crystalline powder that is odorless and nonhygroscopic. It exhibits a clean, sweet taste with no metallic or bitter notes. The sweet taste will linger like those of most high-intensity sweeteners. It forms synergistic blends with acesulfame K, cyclamate, or saccharin. The melting point of alitame is 136–147°C. The unique amide group is in part responsible for alitame's intense sweetness and unique stability characteristics compared with those of aspartame.

**Isoelectric point**—The pH level at which the number of positive charges is equal to the number of negative charges.

**Cyclize**—To form a ring structure in a chemical compound.

**Solubility.** Alitame is soluble in water and forms clear solutions. Its isoelectric point is 5.7. This is also the pH at which alitame is least soluble (13% at 25°C) (6). It is soluble in polar solvents such as methanol, ethanol, and propylene glycol. It is not soluble in nonpolar solvents such as fats, oils, or chloroform. The solubility of alitame increases with increasing temperature and with pH levels greater or less than the isoelectric point.

**Stability.** Because of its unique amide group, alitame exhibits superior stability under a variety of conditions. It is less likely to hydrolyze than the methyl ester of aspartame. The half-life of alitame in aqueous solutions at pH 7–8 and 100°C ranges from hours to days (7). The effects of pH and temperature on the solubility of alitame are shown in Table 2-5. The dipeptide bond of alitame can hydrolyze, forming two final reaction products: aspartic acid and the alanine amide (Fig. 2-7). These end products do not exhibit sweetness. Alitame is stable in carbonated beverages and can withstand the pH levels typical of soft drinks (pH 2–4). Alitame does not cyclize. At neutral pH under aqueous conditions, it is stable for more than a year (7).

**TABLE 2-5.** Solubility[a] of Alitame as a Function of pH and Temperature[b]

| pH | 5°C | 20°C | 30°C | 40°C | 50°C |
|-----|------|------|------|------|------|
| 2.0 | 41.7 | 48.7 | 56.4 | 50.3 | 54.0 |
| 3.0 | 32.2 | 39.2 | 46.5 | 50.9 | 53.9 |
| 4.0 | 12.9 | 13.9 | 17.3 | 20.4 | 37.6 |
| 5.0 | 11.7 | 12.8 | 14.9 | 16.8 | 29.2 |
| 6.0 | 11.6 | 13.2 | 14.9 | 19.5 | 32.8 |
| 7.0 | 11.8 | 14.3 | 17.6 | 29.5 | 51.8 |
| 8.0 | 14.8 | 24.9 | 46.8 | 56.2 | 52.1 |

[a] Water solubility (%, w/v).
[b] Reprinted, with permission, from (7).

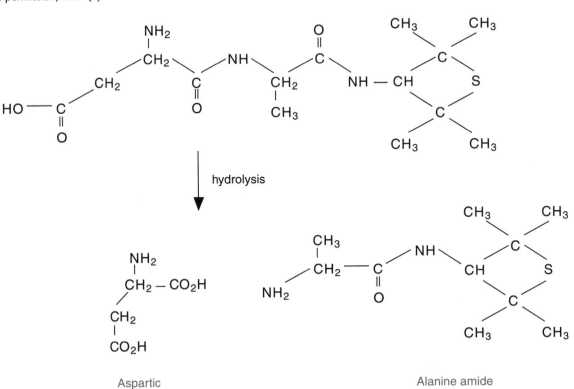

hydrolysis

Aspartic acid

Alanine amide

**Fig. 2-7.** Hydrolysis of alitame.

Because it is stable during heating, alitame can be used in processed foods such as baked goods. Alitame participates in the Maillard browning reaction by providing the –NH group. Therefore, if large amounts of reducing sugars (providing the carbonyl group) are present in the formula, loss of sweetness can occur. At pH <4, off-flavors can form when sodium bisulfite, ascorbic acid, and some caramel colors are also present (7).

**Analytical determinations.** The methods of determination are essentially the same as those for aspartame, since both compounds are dipeptides. The analytical procedure most commonly used to detect alitame or its degradation products is extraction followed by HPLC analysis.

## ACESULFAME POTASSIUM

Acesulfame potassium, or acesulfame K, is a white, crystalline, nonhygroscopic powder. It has a clean, sweet taste that has a rapid onset. At high concentrations, bitter notes or a chemical synthetic note may be detected. Acesulfame K forms synergistic blends with cyclamate and aspartame and with the nutritive sweetener fructose and the sugar alcohols isomalt and sorbitol. It is extremely stable in its dry state. There is no clear melting point for the compound, but it does begin to decompose at temperatures >200°C.

**Solubility.** Acesulfame K dissolves readily in water, forming a clear solution. Solubility increases with increasing temperature (Table 2-6). It is only slightly soluble in organic solvents such as methanol, ethanol, and glycerol.

**Stability.** Acesulfame K is stable in aqueous solutions over a wide range of temperatures and pH levels (Table 2-7). At pH <3, acesulfame K is slightly less stable. However, studies have shown only a small percentage of decomposition during a six-month period (6). Acesulfame K is stable in its dry state, even at high temperatures. Therefore, the sweetener can withstand the temperatures encountered during baking, sterilization, and pasteurization. It is not utilized by microorganisms and is therefore not subject to microbial breakdown.

**Analytical determinations.** Chromatographic methods are used to determine the presence and quantity of acesulfame K. Thin-layer chromatography can be used for the pure substance. In foods, extraction procedures followed by injection into HPLC with a UV detection system is most often utilized. Ion chromatography can also be used in conjunction with a conductivity detector (8).

## SUCRALOSE

Sucralose is a free-flowing, white, crystalline powder. It is extremely stable in its dry state and can be stored at 20°C for several years with no degradation. Sucralose is also available in a stable liquid

**TABLE 2-6.** Solubility of Acesulfame K in Water[a]

| Temperature (°C) | Solubility (g/L) |
|---|---|
| 0 | ~150 |
| 10 | ~210 |
| 20 | ~270 |
| 30 | ~360 |
| 40 | ~460 |
| 50 | ~580 |
| 70 | ~830 |
| 100 | ~1,300 |

[a] Reprinted, with permission, from (8).

**TABLE 2-7.** Stability of Acesulfame K in Buffered Aqueous Solutions at 100°C[a]

| pH | Half-Life |
|---|---|
| 2.6 | ~20 hr |
| 3.0 | ~52 hr |
| 4.0 | ~15 days |
| 5.0 | >50 days |
| 7.0 | >50 days |

[a] Reprinted, with permission, from (8).

concentrate form to which preservatives are added to decrease the microbial activity. In either dry or liquid form, sucralose is very stable when heated and withstands baking, pasteurization, and extrusion. The taste of sucralose is similar to that of sucrose. It is very clean and leaves no aftertastes. Sucralose blends synergistically with cyclamate and acesulfame K.

**Solubility.** Sucralose is soluble in water, ethanol, and methanol at 28.2 g/100 ml at 20°C. It is not soluble in fats and oils. Solubility increases with increasing temperature (Fig. 2-8). Sucralose is also soluble over a wide pH range (Fig. 2-9), although solubility decreases slightly with increasing pH.

**Stability.** Because of the three substituted sites (at which chlorine replaces a hydroxyl group on the sucrose molecule), the reactivity of sucralose is much lower than that sucrose. For example, under acidic conditions, sucrose hydrolyzes to its component sugars, glucose and fructose. Sucralose hydrolyzes under highly acidic conditions, and hydrolysis increases with increasing temperatures. However, the rate of hydrolysis is much lower than that of sucrose (7). Since the primary reaction sites are substituted, sucralose is also less chemically reactive than sucrose. In food systems, sucralose does not interact with other food molecules.

In aqueous systems, sucralose is stable over a wide range of pH. At pH 3 or lower, some hydrolysis occurs, but the amount is very small, and at pH 4–7.5, virtually no sucralose is lost when it is stored at 30°C for a year (Fig. 2-10).

**Analytical determinations.** There are more than 50 developed methods that can be used for the determination of sucralose as a pure substance and for the detection of sucralose in food systems. The most com-

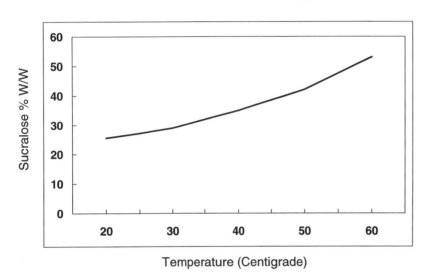

**Fig. 2-8.** Effect of temperature on the solubility of sucralose. (Courtesy McNeil Specialty Products Company)

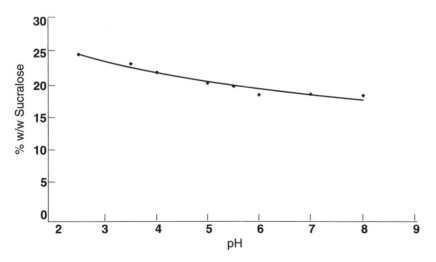

**Fig. 2-9.** Effect of pH on the solubility of sucralose at 20°C. (Courtesy McNeil Specialty Products Company)

mon for quantitation of sucralose in food systems is HPLC in conjunction with a *refractive index* detector.

Because, like sucrose, sucralose refracts light, the refractive index method can be used for the rapid determination of sucralose. An automated refractometer, which is designed to measure sucrose concentration as *degrees Brix*, can also be used to measure sucralose, but the automatic temperature correction mode (called the "TC" mode) cannot be used. Because the prism of the refractometer heats up over time and the refractive index calculation depends on temperature, the TC mode includes a correction factor to account for the temperature increase. The Brix-refractive index correlation holds true for sucrose and sucralose solutions at room temperature but not at elevated temperatures. Thus, the refractive index calculated on an automated refractometer would be incorrect for sucralose solutions at elevated temperatures. In addition, the refractometer cannot accurately measure sucralose at the low concentrations at which it is often used in food applications.

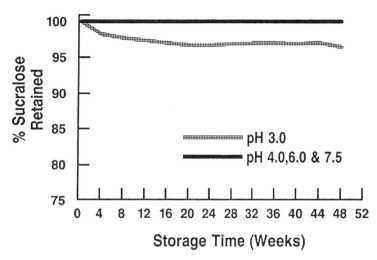

**Fig. 2-10.** Effect of pH on the aqueous stability of sucralose at 30°C. (Reprinted, with permission, from G. A. Miller, Sucralose, pages 173-195 in: [5])

# Naturally Occurring High-Intensity Sweeteners

## THAUMATIN

Thaumatin, a cream-colored, proteinaceous powder, is extracted from the fruit of *Thaumatococcus daniellii*. It is commercially available in the aluminum cation form (herein referred to as thaumatin), which is intensely sweet and stabilizes the color and sweetness of naturally occurring thaumatin. It is stable in its powder form and blends synergistically with acesulfame K, stevioside, and saccharin. Thaumatin is well known (and is perhaps used most often) for its flavor-enhancing capabilities. It is known to enhance the flavors of peppermint, spearmint, coffee, and ginger. The sweetness of thaumatin develops slowly and has a characteristic licorice aftertaste that can linger.

**Solubility.** Thaumatin is very soluble in water and is also soluble in ethanol, propanol, glycerol, and propylene glycol. It is insoluble in acetone and ether. Sixty percent solutions of aqueous thaumatin can be easily prepared (6).

**Stability.** Solutions of thaumatin in water can be heated without loss of sweetness. However, the aqueous stability of thaumatin does depend on the concentration of the solution, the amount of oxygen

**Refractive index**—Physical property of a substance that relates to how light is refracted from the material. Usually used to indirectly measure some other property, such as soluble solids (i.e., the total sugars in solution).

**Degrees Brix (°Brix)**— Measure of the density or concentration of a sugar solution. The degrees Brix equal the weight percent of sucrose in the solution.

present, certain salts, certain *polyelectrolytes*, and pH. Solutions of thaumatin at room temperature are stable at pH 2–10; maximum stability of aqueous solutions is at pH 2.8–3.0 (6). Solutions can be pasteurized without loss of sweetness at pH 2.8–3.5 and can be heated at 100°C for many hours and remain sweet. The thermal stability of an aqueous solution depends on several factors that influence the thermal denaturation of the protein molecule. Once the protein denatures, the molecular configuration responsible for the sweetness changes and the sweetness is lost. Thaumatin also contains disulfide bonds, which, if altered, also change the molecular conformation, and again sweetness can be lost. The alteration of the disulfide bonds can occur as a result of heat denaturation as well as chemical cleavage.

**Analytical determinations.** Since thaumatin is a protein, it can be detected by the usual protein analytical methods. Common methods include gel filtration and ion exchange chromatography.

## STEVIOSIDE

Stevioside is classified as a diterpenoid compound and is one of eight sweet compounds present in the plant *Stevia rebaudiana*. The most widely available commercial form is the stevioside extract. A complete review of the characteristics of all of the stevia compounds is given in *Handbook of Sweeteners* (4). Stevioside in its purest form is a white, crystalline, hygroscopic powder with a melting point of 196–198°C. It is available in levels of 10, 50, and 90% purity. It is generally not used in its pure form because other components from the stevia plant are also extracted. Rebaudioside A, another sweet component of the plant, can be present in stevioside extract and provides better stability and solubility and a better taste profile. The extract can have a bitter taste and unpleasant menthol and even licorice aftertastes. The more rebaudioside A that is present, the less pronounced the aftertastes. Stevioside combines synergistically with glycyrrhizin and is available commercially in a blend with this other natural sweetener. It also forms a synergistic blend with aspartame, cyclamate, and acesulfame K but not with saccharin.

**Solubility.** Stevioside is soluble in water and slightly soluble in ethanol and propylene glycol. Solubility of the stevioside extract increases with increasing levels of rebaudioside A.

**Stability.** Stevioside in its dry state is very stable. It withstands heat and is not subject to browning or fermentation by microorganisms. Aqueous solutions are stable at pH 3–9 but decompose at pH >10. Stevioside retains its sweetness after being held at 100°C for 1 hr at pH 3–9. It is therefore stable under the processing conditions of baking and pasteurization.

**Analytical determinations.** All stevia compounds are detectable by HPLC. For pure quantitation and isolation and detection in food sys-

**Polyelectrolyte**—Natural or synthetic substance containing constituents that provide ionic conductivity.

tems, extraction followed by detection with HPLC is the method most commonly used (4).

## GLYCYRRHIZIN

Glycyrrhizin is classified as a terpenoid glycoside, or a triterpenoid, and is isolated from the licorice-root plant, *Glycyrrhiza glabra* L. The compound itself is intensely sweet and has a strong licorice flavor that limits its use as a sweetener in many food applications. The pure isolated form is a colorless crystal. It is an acid compound, and thus when extracted, it is a calcium, potassium, or magnesium salt. The extract also contains other plant components such as starches, proteins, and flavonoids. Commercially, the extract is most widely available as the ammonium salt of glycyrrhizic acid (referred to herein as glycyrrhizin). Glycyrrhizin combines synergistically with stevioside and is available as a blend with that sweetener.

**Solubility.** Glycyrrhizin (as the ammonium salt) is soluble in both hot and cold water. The other forms (calcium, potassium, or magnesium salt) are only slightly soluble in cold water but are soluble in hot water. The hot aqueous solutions of the calcium salt and the free glycyrrhizic acid form a gel upon cooling (3).

**Stability.** Glycyrrhizin is stable in its dry form and is stable when heated. In aqueous solutions, it is reasonably stable when heated. At pH <4.5, it precipitates from solution.

**Analytical determinations.** Glycyrrhizin is most often detected in food systems by extraction techniques followed by HPLC (3).

## References

1. Alexander, R. J. 1998. *Sweeteners: Nutritive.* American Association of Cereal Chemists, St. Paul, MN.
2. Terada, H., and Sabake, Y. 1985. J. Chromatogr. Anal. Chem. 346:333.
3. Krutosikova, A., and Uher, M. 1992. *Natural and Synthetic Sweet Substances.* Ellis Horwood, New York.
4. Marie, S., and Piggott, J. R. 1991. *Handbook of Sweeteners.* AVI, New York.
5. O'Brien Nabors, L., and Gelardi, R. C., Eds. 1991. *Alternative Sweeteners,* 2nd ed. Marcel Dekker, New York.
6. Grenby, T. H. 1989. *Progress in Sweeteners.* Elsevier, New York.
7. Grenby, T. H., Ed. 1996. *Advances in Sweeteners.* Blackie Academic & Professional, Glasgow, Scotland.
8. Mayer, D. G., and Kemper, F. H., Eds. 1991. *Acesulfame–K.* Marcel Dekker, New York.

# Properties of Sugar Alcohols

Sugar alcohols are an important group of sweeteners. The name "sugar alcohol" is a bit misleading because the molecular structure is not that of a sugar. Sugar alcohols are derived from sugars by hydrogenation of the sugar molecule, a process that chemically reduces the carbonyl group to the –OH chemical group, which is called an alcohol or hydroxyl group (Fig. 3-1). Hence, the commonly used name, sugar alcohols. Sugar alcohols are also referred to as polyols, polyhydric alcohols, or polyalcohols, all meaning "containing many –OH groups." "Polyols" has been submitted to the Food and Drug Administration as the industry-preferred term. The common *monosaccharide* sugar alcohols are sorbitol, mannitol, and xylitol. The common disaccharide sugar alcohols are isomalt, lactitol, and maltitol. These substances also occur naturally in many plants and fruits.

Sugar alcohols are considered nutritive sweeteners because they have caloric value. They are important in the development of foods because they are noncariogenic and do not raise blood glucose to the levels that sucrose does (these features are discussed in more detail in Chapter 7). One of the purposes of sucrose is to provide bulk to a food product. In reduced-calorie foods, sugar alcohols can provide the bulk that high-intensity sweeteners alone cannot. Thus, they are often used in combination with high-intensity sweeteners. Some also provide sweetness on their own. Their relative sweetness, which depends upon concentration, ranges from 0.3 to 1 (Fig. 3-2) but can vary somewhat when determined by different methods. In their dry form, most sugar alcohols have a cooling effect upon the tongue, resulting from the negative heat of solution. The greater the negative number, the greater the cooling effect (Fig. 3-3). The primary uses of sugar alcohols in food applications are listed in Table 3-1.

## General Comparisons

Because of their structure, sugar alcohols are generally less chemically reactive than sucrose or other nutritive sweeteners such as corn syrup or honey. Sugar alcohols do not contain the reactive carbonyl

**In This Chapter:**

General Comparisons

Individual Sugar Alcohols
  Sorbitol
  Mannitol
  Xylitol
  Lactitol
  Maltitol
  Isomalt
  Hydrogenated Starch
    Syrups

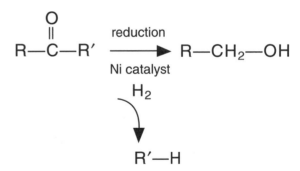

**Fig. 3-1.** Reduction of a carbonyl group to an alcohol group.

**Monosaccharide**—A carbohydrate containing a single sugar unit, usually composed of five or six carbon atoms, existing in a furanose (five-membered ring) or pyranose (six-membered ring) form.

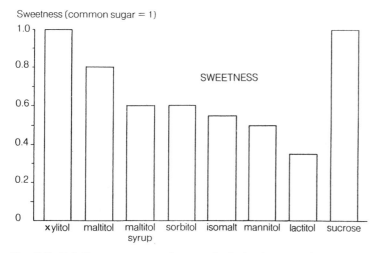

**Fig. 3-2.** Relative sweetness of sugar alcohols. (Reprinted, with permission, from [1])

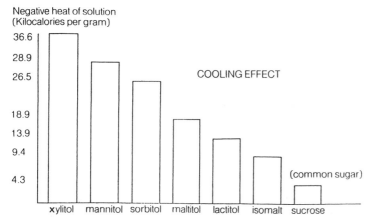

**Fig. 3-3.** Cooling effects of sugar alcohols. (Reprinted, with permission, from [1])

group (C=O) necessary for participation in the Maillard browning reaction. They are also more resistant to enzymatic action, microbial attack, and fermentation by yeasts and more stable under conditions of heat and varying pH.

The physical properties of the individual sugar alcohols vary. Their melting points range from 76 to 168°C (Table 3-2). Unlike sucrose, the solubility of the sugar alcohols strongly depends upon temperature (Fig. 3-4). The slope of the solubility line for sucrose is relatively flat, while those of the sugar alcohols are greater, indicating the dependence on temperature. The solubilities of sugar alcohols range from about 15 to 70 g/100 g of water at 25°C. Sugar alcohols also differ in hygroscopicity; sorbitol and maltitol are very hygroscopic and mannitol and isomalt are nonhygroscopic. The hygroscopicity of the sugar alcohols, in ascending order, is mannitol < isomalt < lactitol < xylitol < sorbitol (crystalline) < maltitol < sorbitol (syrup). This property is important for the reduction of the water activity in food systems, and sorbitol is often used for this purpose. Sugar alcohols also effectively control crystallization. In general, sugar alcohol solutions are less viscous than sucrose solutions at the same concentration. This reduced viscosity affects the nu-

**TABLE 3-1.** Primary Applications of Sugar Alcohols in Foods

| Sugar Alcohol | Uses |
| --- | --- |
| Xylitol | Jellies, chewing gum, coatings for gum, mint-flavored candies |
| Mannitol | Dusting powder, chewing gums, effervescent products |
| Sorbitol | Chewing gum, tablets, candies, humectants, plasticizers |
| Sorbitol (liquid) | Hard candies, baked goods, humectants, plasticizers |
| Isomalt | Chewing gum, dusting powder |
| Lactitol | Candies, frozen desserts, jams and jellies, chocolate, dusting powder, bulking agent, baked products |
| Maltitol | Hard candies, chewing gum, chocolate |
| HMS[a] | Hard candies, chewing gum, jellies |
| HGS[b] | Confections |

[a] Hydrogenated maltose syrup
[b] Hydrogenated glucose syrup.

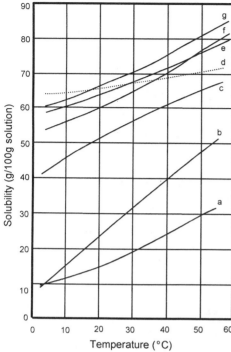

**Fig. 3-4.** Solubility of different polyols with increasing temperature: a, mannitol; b, isomalt; c, lactitol; d, sucrose; e, maltitol; f, xylitol; g, sorbitol. (Reprinted, with permission, from [2])

**TABLE 3-2.** Physical Properties of Sugar Alcohols

| Sugar Alcohol | Molecular Formula | Molecular Weight | Melting Point (°C) |
|---|---|---|---|
| Xylitol | $C_5H_{12}O_5$ | 152 | 92–96 |
| Mannitol | $C_6H_{14}O_6$ | 182 | 165–168 |
| Sorbitol | $C_6H_{14}O_6$ | 182 | 88–98 |
| Isomalt | $C_{12}H_{26}O_{12}$ | 346 | 148–151 |
| Lactitol | | | |
| Anhydrate | $C_{12}H_{26}O_{12}$ | 346 | 145–155 |
| Monohydrate | $C_{12}H_{26}O_{12} \cdot H_2O$ | 364 | 94–100 |
| Maltitol | $C_{12}H_{26}O_{12}$ | 346 | 146–147 |

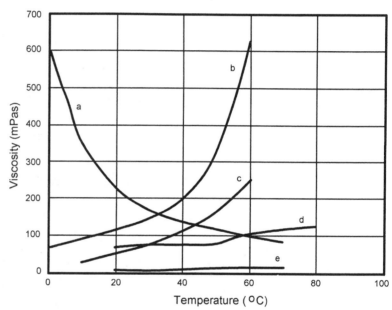

**Fig. 3-5.** Viscosity of different saturated polyol solutions with increasing temperature: a, sucrose; b, sorbitol; c, xylitol; d, maltitol; e, isomalt. (Source: [3])

cleation and crystal growth processes, and so sugar alcohols are added to foods to inhibit unwanted crystallization. The viscosities of various sugar alcohol saturated solutions are shown in Figure 3-5.

Both gas chromatography and high-performance liquid chromatography (HPLC) methods have been developed for the analytical detection and quantification of sugar alcohols (4,5).

Sorbitol, xylitol, and maltitol crystals are shown in Figure 3-6, and the chemical and physical properties of individual sugar alcohols are discussed in more detail in the following sections.

# Individual Sugar Alcohols

## SORBITOL

Sorbitol is a monosaccharide sugar alcohol derived by hydrogenating either fructose or glucose. It is available commercially in three

**Fig. 3-6.** Sugar alcohol crystals. **A**, Sorbitol, **B**, xylitol, and **C**, maltitol. (Courtesy Roquette Freres)

**Polymorphic**—Having the ability to crystallize in more than one three-dimensional arrangement.

**Chelate**—To combine with to form a ring.

forms, crystalline, liquid, and instant, all of which exhibit a sweet, cooling taste. The crystalline form is a white, free-flowing powder. Sorbitol is *polymorphic*; that is, it is able to exist in different crystalline forms. The γ crystalline form, also often referred to as the seed-grade form, is the only stable one. These crystals are slightly hygroscopic and have a melting point of about 98°C. The other two forms, α and β, are less stable and have melting points of approximately 88 and 95°C, respectively. The liquid syrup is a clear solution and is usually a concentration of about 70% sorbitol in water. Sorbitol in solution is generally more hygroscopic than the crystalline form. Instant sorbitol is also available and is manufactured by spray drying a concentrated sorbitol solution. This product is readily soluble and has a lower density than the crystalline powder form. Care must be taken to properly store all sorbitol forms to prevent the absorption of moisture.

Because sorbitol is hygroscopic, it is effective in lowering the water activity of foods. The effects of glycerol, sorbitol, and sucrose on water activity are compared in Figure 3-7. Sorbitol decomposes at 150°C and is therefore stable at baking and boiling temperatures. It also *chelates* certain multivalent cations such as iron and copper.

Sorbitol is freely soluble in water (68 g/100 g of water at 25°C). It is also soluble in dilute acetic acid, methanol, and warm ethanol, but it is not soluble in organic solvents. Seventy percent solutions crystallize at temperatures <10°C over time (6). Some commercially available solutions contain oligosaccharides to help inhibit crystallization.

## MANNITOL

Mannitol is a monosaccharide derived by hydrogenating fructose or mannose. It is a white, crystalline powder with a melting point of 165–168°C. It is essentially nonhygroscopic and is often used as a dusting agent or anticaking agent in the confectionery industry. It has a clean, sweet taste that is less cooling than that of xylitol. The viscosities of mannitol and sorbitol solutions are very similar. Mannitol can chelate metals such as iron, copper, and nickel.

Mannitol is the least soluble sugar alcohol (about 17 g/100 g of water at 20°C). It is sparingly soluble in organic solvents such as ethanol and is mostly insoluble in ether.

## XYLITOL

Xylitol is derived from the hydrogenation of the monosaccharide xylose and is available as a white, odorless, crystalline powder. Its melting point is 92–96°C. Xylitol exhibits a clean, sweet taste and in powder form has a cooling effect upon the tongue. Its relative sweetness is very close to that of sucrose, and it has very low hygroscopicity.

The solubility of xylitol is closest to that of sucrose at room temperature. It is very soluble in water (63 g/100 g of water at 20°C) and is slightly soluble in ethanol and methanol.

## LACTITOL

Lactitol is a disaccharide sugar alcohol derived by hydrogenation of the glucose portion of lactose. It exists in an anhydrous form and in two crystalline forms, *monohydrate* and *dihydrate*. In the monohydrate form, there is one molecule of water on the lactitol crystal; in the dihydrate form, there are two. Lactitol has a clean, sweet taste with a very low cooling effect. The melting point of the monohydrate form is 94–100°C; that of the dihydrate form is 76–78°C. When heated to 100°C, the monohydrate crystal reverts to its anhydrous form. Lactitol is not hydrolyzed by the enzyme lactase, which hydrolyzes lactose. Lactitol has very low hygroscopicity, lower than that of sucrose.

When heated to 170–240°C, lactitol can decompose by losing the water molecules to form sorbitol, lactitan, and lower saccharides. Lactitol's stability at low pH levels is similar to that of lactose. It can hydrolyze when held at pH 1–2 at 100°C (6).

The solubility of lactitol is similar to that of glucose. It is very soluble in water, 55 g/100 g at 25°C. Lactitol does not cause a sandy texture in products such as ice cream, in which the solubility of lactose can be a problem.

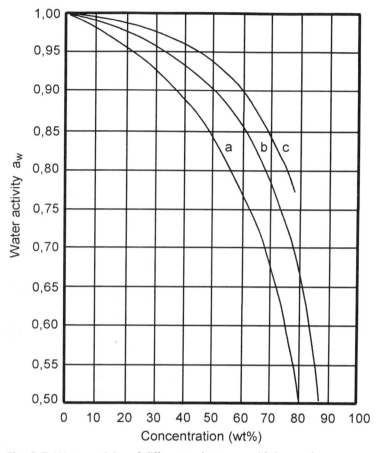

**Fig. 3-7.** Water activity of different substances with increasing concentration: a, glycerol; b, sorbitol; and c, sucrose. (Source: I. Willibald-Ettle and H. Schiweck, Properties and applications of isomalt and other bulk sweeteners, pages 134-149 in: [6])

## MALTITOL

Maltitol is a white, crystalline, odorless powder that is derived by the hydrogenation of maltose. It exhibits a clean, sweet taste with a very low cooling effect. Its sweetness is very similar to that of sucrose. The crystalline form melts at 146–147°C. It exhibits very low hygroscopicity. It is stable at pH of 5–7, but at lower pH levels and especially at higher temperatures, maltitol can hydrolyze. It can also be cleaved by enzymes.

**Monohydrate**—A compound that contains one molecule of water.

**Dihydrate**—A compound that contains two molecules of water.

Maltitol is very soluble in water (66 g/100 g at 25°C). It is more soluble than sucrose at temperatures >40°C (Fig. 3-4).

## ISOMALT

Isomalt, derived by hydrogenating sucrose, is a mixture of the resultant two disaccharide alcohols: glucomannitol and glucosorbitol. It is a white, crystalline powder with a melting point of 148–151°C. It has very low hygroscopicity and is often used in the making of hard candy. It has a very low cooling effect and a clean, sweet taste similar to that of sucrose. It hydrolyzes under acid conditions to yield glucose, sorbitol, and mannitol. It is more stable to hydrolysis than sucrose.

Its solubility is very low (27 g/100 g of water at 25°C) and is most similar to that of mannitol. It has a tendency to crystallize out of solution.

## HYDROGENATED STARCH SYRUPS

Hydrogenated starch syrups are blends of sugar alcohols hydrogenated from mixtures of starch hydrolysis products. The syrups generally contain 70–75% solids and are very resistant to crystallization. There are several different types available, including hydrogenated glucose syrups, maltitol syrups, and sorbitol syrups. End product syrups often contain sorbitol, maltitol, and other hydrogenated polysaccharides.

A wide range of end products can be obtained by altering the starting material and the hydrogenation conditions. Therefore, viscosity, hygroscopicity, and sweetness can be tailored to meet the product developer's needs. In general, syrups that contain >50% sorbitol are called sorbitol syrups, and those that contain >50% maltitol are called maltitol syrups or hydrogenated glucose syrups. If no specific sugar alcohol is present as a major component, the syrup is called a hydrogenated starch hydrolysate. The syrups are synergistic with high-intensity sweeteners. At low pH, the syrups can undergo hydrolysis, which alters hygroscopicity and viscosity. Because the properties of the syrups can vary widely, users must obtain specific information for a particular product.

## References

1. Bär, A. 1991. Xylitol. Pages 349-379 in: *Alternative Sweeteners,* 2nd ed. L. O'Brien Nabors and R. C. Gelardi, Eds. Marcel Dekker, New York.
2. Schiweck, H. 1994. Sugar alcohols. Pages 413-436 in: *Ullman's Encyclopedia of Industrial Chemistry,* 5th ed. Vol. A25. B. Elvers, S. Hawkins, and W. Russey, Eds. VCH Verlagsgesellschaft, Weinheim.
3. Weber, W. 1994. Naschen ohne Karies. Süßwaren 1-2, 12-13.
4. Samarco, E. C., and Parente, E. S. 1982. Automated high pressure liquid chromatographic system for determination of mannitol, sorbitol, and xylitol in chewing gums and confections (sugar substitutes). J. Assoc. Off. Anal. Chem. 65:76-78.

5. Daniels, D. H., Warner, C. R., and Fazio, T. 1982. Gas chromatographic determination of sorbitol, mannitol, and xylitol in chewing gum and sorbitol mints. J. Assoc. Off. Anal. Chem. 65:588-591.
6. Grenby, T. H., Ed. 1996. *Advances in Sweeteners*. Blackie Academic & Professional, Glasgow, Scotland.

# Confectionery

The confectionery industry relies heavily on nutritive sweeteners for the many physical and chemical properties that they impart. The most commonly used sweeteners, sucrose, dextrose (glucose), and corn syrups, are fundamental in the production of confectionery items such as hard candy, caramel, taffy, chewing gum, chocolate, and gummed candies. In addition to their function in these items, they are widely used around the world because they are low in cost, readily available, and easy to use during processing.

The formulations of many sweetened confections are centered around the properties of sucrose, dextrose, and corn syrups. Depending on the final confection, these sweeteners provide sweetness, mouthfeel or body, graining or crystallization, texture, hardness or softness, shelf life, flavors, and colors. The formulations of many sweetened confections were developed decades or even centuries ago, and the processing parameters used to meet today's production requirements are very well known. The uses of nutritive sweeteners in confectionery applications are reviewed elsewhere (1).

The impact of daily diet and nutrition on overall health and wellness has been studied, and consumers have become informed about the effects that foods can have on their well being. Awareness of issues related to diet and weight gain and obesity, dental caries, and diabetic metabolism has helped to create a market for sugar-free and reduced-calorie products. These foods are made with alternative sweeteners, and a wide array of products, including confections, is currently available in the marketplace.

Many difficult technical challenges arise during the development of these types of confectionery products. The formulations, processing needs, and final product properties of hard candies obviously differ from those of chocolates, chewing gum, and caramels. Fortunately, many recent innovations in alternative sweetening, including the use of sugar alcohols and high-intensity sweeteners, have helped to solve these technical issues.

## Alternative Sweeteners Used in Confections

The use of alternative sweeteners in confections was fairly limited prior to 1992 in the United States because the Food and Drug

**TABLE 4-1.** Caloric Values for Sugar Alcohols Allowed by the U.S. Food and Drug Administration

| Sugar Alcohol | Calories/gram |
| --- | --- |
| Hydrogenated starch hydrolysates | 3.0 |
| Maltitol | 2.1 |
| Sorbitol | 2.6 |
| Xylitol | 2.4 |
| Isomalt | 2.0 |
| Lactitol | 2.0 |
| Mannitol | 1.6 |

Administration (FDA) had banned the use of nonnutritive ingredients in confectionery products unless they served specific functional purposes. The FDA clarified this regulation in its 1980 compliance policy guide, which stated, "The use of nonnutritive artificial sweeteners in confectionery for the purpose of caloric reduction is not considered to be a practical functional purpose" (2). In 1992, the compliance policy guide was revised to allow the use of nonnutritive sweeteners in confectionery products.

Sugar alcohols were used at first in items such as chewing gums and breath mints. These products were marketed as promoting dental health by reducing caries. In 1992, a value of 4 calories per gram was used in the United States for all sugar alcohols, the same number of calories found in nutritive sweeteners. Therefore, there was no advantage in replacing a nutritive sweetener with a sugar alcohol in the development of a reduced-calorie product. This changed in 1994, when the FDA allowed the use of reduced caloric values for specific sugar alcohols. These caloric values are shown in Table 4-1. Currently in the United States and in several other countries, both high-intensity and sugar alcohol alternative sweeteners are used in the production of sugar-free and reduced-calorie confections. The specific alternative sweeteners that are commonly used in confectionery applications are described below.

## HIGH-INTENSITY SWEETENERS

High-intensity sweeteners are used in sugar-free and reduced-calorie confections to provide the sweetness associated with the traditional products, but unlike sucrose and corn syrups, they do not add bulk. Therefore, high-intensity sweeteners are used in combination with bulking agents such as *polydextrose*, *maltodextrins*, and sugar alcohols in the reformulated products. The high-intensity sweeteners most widely used in confections are acesulfame K, aspartame, alitame, cyclamates, saccharin, sucralose, and thaumatin.

**Acesulfame potassium.** Acesulfame potassium, or acesulfame K, is suitable for use in hard, soft, and chocolate confections. It is very heat stable and can therefore be added during the boiling step in the making of hard candy, when temperatures can be >148°C (3). Because of its solubility, it can also be dissolved in sugar alcohol syrups, added as an aqueous solution, or added with other ingredients such as flavors or colors (4). It is also stable at various pH levels and can be added to a wide range of confectionery products without degrading (5).

**Aspartame.** Aspartame is labile when heated and outside the pH range of 3 to 5. However, aspartame is still a viable option for use in confections. It can be added with colors and flavors after any heat-processing step, and a more heat-stable, encapsulated form can be used to minimize the loss of sweetness that occurs with heat and varia-

**Polydextrose**—A nonsweet polymer of glucose, sorbitol, and citric acid (89:10:1) commonly used to provide bulk in alternatively sweetened foods.

**Maltodextrins**—Nonsweet compounds (DE = 5–20) made from hydrolyzed starches.

tions in pH. Some loss of sweetness can also occur as a result of its participation in the Maillard browning reaction. Aspartame provides clean, sweet flavors that enhance fruit-based or fruit-flavored candies. Its stability is excellent in hard candies and in low-moisture systems such as gelled candies and fruit chews (6).

**Alitame.** Because it is very stable, alitame can be used in many confectionery applications. It withstands heat and different pH levels and can therefore be added during various processing stages. However, because it is susceptible to the Maillard browning reaction, loss of sweetness can occur in certain processing situations, e.g., the production of caramels.

**Cyclamates.** Although currently banned in the United States, cyclamates are approved for use in some other countries and are added to many confectionery products in those countries. They are best used in combination with saccharin because they mask saccharin's off-flavors and saccharin enhances their sweetening power (7).

**Saccharin.** Although it is still used in many applications, saccharin is not used in the confectionery industry as widely as it once was. It is stable when heated and under many of the processing conditions of hard, soft, and chocolate confections, but it can contribute to off-flavors in the final product (7). Other approved high-intensity sweeteners have replaced saccharin and provide cleaner-tasting confections.

**Sucralose.** Sucralose is a suitable sweetener for confections because it is very stable when heated and tolerates various levels of pH. It is also soluble and is easily incorporated into the various processing steps of confectionery products. Since it does not interact with other food ingredients, loss of sweetness during processing is minimal. It remains stable during storage in products such as chocolate and marshmallows (7).

**Thaumatin.** Thaumatin is a natural high-intensity sweetener used mainly in chewing gum applications. It is not allowed as a sweetening agent in the United States, but it is used as a flavor enhancer. It is stable at high temperatures and under acidic and basic pH conditions. However, it exhibits a lingering licorice-like flavor that limits its use in most confectionery applications (8). It masks the synthetic taste of some nonnutritive sweeteners and reduces the amount of nonnutritive sweeteners needed in chewing gum applications (9).

## SUGAR ALCOHOLS

Sugar alcohols can help compensate for the loss of bulk that occurs when corn syrups, dextrose, and sucrose are removed from traditional confectionery formulas, and many also provide sweetness and other properties that are essential to the final product. Thus, they are often called *bulk sweeteners*. Their chemical and physical properties are fully reviewed in Chapter 3. These properties as they apply to confections are discussed here.

**Bulk sweetener**—Sweetener that also adds bulk.

**Sorbitol.** Sorbitol was one of the first sugar alcohols used in the confectionery industry. It is considered a standard ingredient in chewing gum and tablet formulas because of its compressibility. Sorbitol is polymorphic and exhibits three different crystalline structures: the α structure, which is the least stable; the β structure, which is very unstable and very hygroscopic; and the γ structure, which is the most stable. The γ structure is the most desirable for confectionery products because it helps ensure stability by decreasing moisture absorption (10). Because sorbitol is about 60% as sweet as sucrose, some formulations that use sorbitol also include high-intensity sweeteners to achieve the desired sweetness level in the final product.

**Mannitol.** Mannitol has very low solubility and is therefore available only in powdered or crystalline form. It also exhibits very low hygroscopicity. Because of these properties, it is often used as a dusting agent in confections such as chewing gum, in tableted confections and chocolates, as a crystal inhibitor in hard candies, and as a release agent in molds for gelled confections. Small amounts of mannitol are present in some commercially available sorbitol solutions, where it helps to inhibit crystallization. Because mannitol is about 50–65% as sweet as sucrose, a high-intensity sweetener may be necessary to achieve desired sweetness levels in products such as chocolates.

**Maltitol.** Crystalline maltitol is one of the sweetest sugar alcohols, providing about 90% of the sweetness of sucrose. It has negligible cooling effects and is therefore used in confectionery applications such as chocolates. The melting point and solubility of maltitol are very similar to those of sucrose, so the processing conditions in many confectionery applications need not be changed.

**Xylitol.** Xylitol has the greatest cooling effect of all the sugar alcohols and is therefore used in confectionery applications where this is a desirable attribute, e.g., in chewing gums, tableted mints, and some hard and soft candies. It is moderately hygroscopic and can be used as a sanding agent in sugar-free confections such as gummed candies (11). As a topical sanding agent, it can aid in the sweetness of the final product, since it is the sweetest of all the sugar alcohols, and it provides the visual appearance of sucrose. The viscosity provided by xylitol is lower than that provided by sucrose, which may necessitate formulation changes such as decreasing the moisture content or increasing the solids content (e.g., with gelling agents or polydextrose) in products such as gelled candies (10,12). Because of the crystallization properties of xylitol, confections such as *fondants*, toffees, and transparent hard candies cannot be formulated with xylitol alone.

**Hydrogenated starch hydrolysates.** Hydrogenated starch hydrolysates (HSHs) can help provide viscosity and cohesiveness in confections. They do not crystallize at low temperatures or at high concentrations, which makes them useful in the development of hard candy and soft candies such as taffy and caramel. HSHs act as crystal inhibitors and can be used to prevent the crystallization of other sugar alcohols such as sorbitol, mannitol, and xylitol (10). Some

**Fondant**—Grained confection often used as an ingredient in the manufacture of other candies such as fudge.

HSHs are hygroscopic, and while this helps to prevent crystallization, it can also cause tackiness or stickiness in the final product. HSHs have low sweetening power and are often used in conjunction with high-intensity sweeteners.

**Lactitol.** Lactitol has the lowest hygroscopicity of the sugar alcohols. This property improves the shelf life stability of confectionery products. In addition, lactitol positively influences flavor release from hard candy confections (13,14). It has a low cooling effect and can be used in many confectionery applications such as chocolates and soft and hard candies. However, it cannot be used as the sole bulk sweetener in hard candy applications because it crystallizes. In its anhydrous form, lactitol can easily be incorporated into the chocolate-manufacturing process.

**Isomalt.** The properties of isomalt are similar to those of sucrose, although it is slightly less soluble and has a higher boiling point in aqueous solutions (13). It is nonhygroscopic and can be used in hard candy applications to inhibit moisture absorption. Because of its low solubility, it has a tendency to crystallize. It is about 50% as sweet as sucrose, so a high-intensity sweetener may be needed to achieve desired sweetness levels in the final product. Because it has a low cooling effect, it can be used in many confectionery applications, e.g., chocolate, hard candy, caramel, chewing gum, and tableted confections. Confections that are hygroscopic can be pan coated with isomalt to help maintain product stability (15).

# Hard Confections

There are two basic types of hard confections: hard candy and tableted confections. Most hard candies are transparent and have a smooth, amorphous, glasslike structure. They are also colored and flavored. Tableted confections are formed by compression and are necessarily hard in nature. They should not fall apart easily. Suitable alternative sweeteners are available for both of these applications to produce sugar-free or reduced-calorie confections.

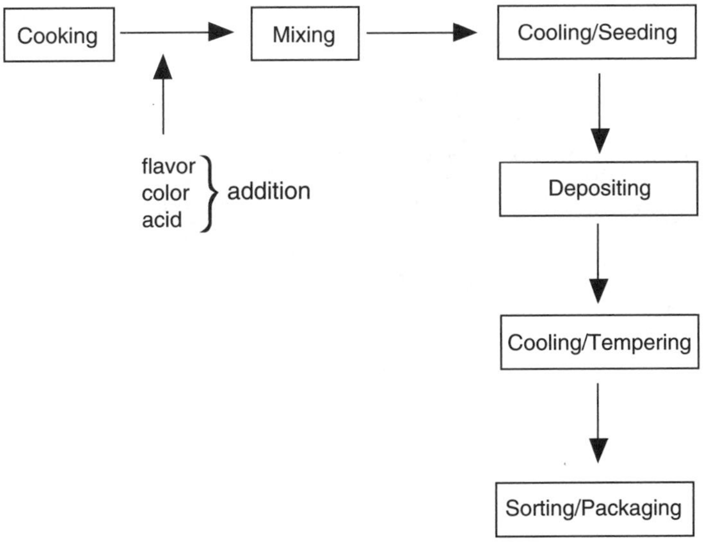

**Fig. 4-1.** Depositing method for the production of hard candies. (Adapted from [16])

## HARD CANDIES

There are two main methods of producing hard candies with alternative sweeteners. The depositing method (Fig. 4-1) is used when the formulation never forms a *plastic* state. In other words, the material is liquid at the temperature (about 90°C) at which it is deposited and formed. This

**Plastic**—Having a stretchable nature.

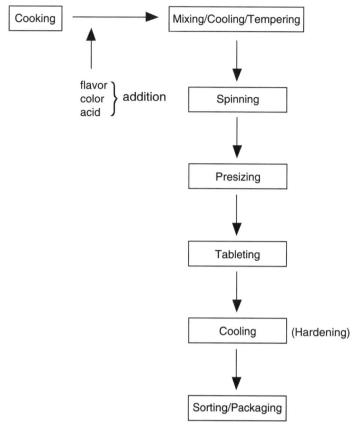

**Fig. 4-2.** Forming and spinning method for the production of hard candies. (Adapted from [16])

**TABLE 4-2.** Typical Hard Candy Formulation in Which Sorbitol Is Used as a Bulk Sweetener[a]

| Ingredient | Amount (%) |
|---|---|
| Sorbitol | 94.06–98.60 |
| Citric, malic, or tartaric acid | 1–1.8 |
| Water | 0.25–3.0 |
| Flavor | 0.04–0.51 |
| Color | 0.01–0.04 |

[a] Adapted from (17).

**Inversion**—The process by which sucrose hydrolyzes to its component sugars, fructose and glucose.

process is used for making sorbitol-, isomalt-, or maltitol-based hard candies. The more traditional process is the spinning and forming method (Fig. 4-2), which can be used to produce hard candies made with isomalt or HSHs. These materials form a plastic that can be spun and formed into separate pieces. Pure crystalline maltitol can also be made by the forming and spinning process. However, it can crystallize at high levels of purity, and the formulation must include a crystal inhibitor.

Some sugar alcohols used as bulking agents or bulk sweeteners are the major components in hard candy formulations. A typical hard candy formulation in which sorbitol is used is shown in Table 4-2. Sugar alcohols work well in the making of hard candies for several reasons. First, because they do not participate in the Maillard browning reaction, discolorations caused by the reaction do not occur. Second, they do not undergo *inversion*. Inversion, which affects sucrose, is the cleaving of the molecule into its monosaccharide components that occurs under conditions of high heat and low pH. The monosaccharides are more hygroscopic than sugar alcohols, resulting in tacky or sticky candies. Since sugar alcohols are not subject to inversion, products with more stability are possible. Finally, sugar alcohols can be heated to 165–198°C before they begin to decompose, while sucrose decomposes at about 150°C.

**Sorbitol.** Sorbitol, one of the first sugar alcohols used in making sugar-free hard candy, can be used as the main base ingredient. However, because it does not have a plastic state during which it can be spun and formed into pieces, the depositing method must be used when sorbitol is the main base ingredient. It may be necessary to adjust the acid-to-sweetener ratio in some formulations since sorbitol is not as sweet as some other sugar alcohols. Because sorbitol is hygroscopic, care must be taken to maintain proper conditions in the processing environment. The relative humidity should be <35%, and the temperature should be about 20–23°C.

Because a melt *endotherm* peak forms when sorbitol-based candies are subjected to differential scanning calorimetry, it has been suggested that these candies are crystalline in nature (17). Therefore, seed-grade sorbitol, which consists of the most stable γ crystalline form, is used to seed the formula in order to set the structure for the final product. Seeding helps to maintain consistent set times from batch to batch by providing approximately the same number of nucleation sites. Sorbitol-based candies should be seeded at 87–90°C, the melting point of the simplest polymorphic form (16). Although the final structure of sorbitol hard candies is crystalline, the crystals are so small that the final hard candy is transparent. This crystalline lattice can exclude the flavors from the candy matrix (16), so emulsifiers and longer mixing times may be needed to incorporate flavors into the mix.

Starchless depositors and plastic molds work best to provide a clean, nonslimy mouthfeel. Because of the hygroscopicity of the final product, packaging films that inhibit transmission of water vapor should be used and the pieces should be individually wrapped. A problem that sometimes occurs during storage is *dry graining*. The hard candy becomes cloudy and opaque when storage temperatures are >37°C. Dry graining occurs in products subjected during processing to excessive shear at temperatures <100°C (below the crystallization point of sorbitol), which creates many seed crystals in the candy mixture.

**Isomalt.** Isomalt can also be used as the main base ingredient in hard candy formulations. These candies can be made by either the depositing method or the traditional spinning and forming process. Because isomalt has lower solubility, a higher boiling point, lower viscosity, and higher *heat capacity* than sucrose (15,18), changes in processing conditions are necessary when isomalt is substituted for sucrose or corn syrup in traditional hard candy formulations. Care must be taken to ensure that all the isomalt crystals are dissolved and melted during boiling. Boiling times and temperatures should be increased. Piping may need to be heated so that the mixture does not cool and crystallize during transfer from one operation to another. Cooling times should be increased to ensure proper setting. With these modifications, high-quality hard candies with good shelf life stability can be produced.

Because of isomalt's low hygroscopicity, the final products do not absorb moisture and become sticky. In addition, isomalt candies can be center filled. The center filling should contain >75% solids to inhibit the moisture migration that results in crystallization in the outer shell near the filling interface (18). Also, if the filling is hygroscopic (e.g., if HSHs or polydextrose was used), a twist wrapping may be necessary to inhibit moisture absorption at the stamped interface seam of the filling and shell.

Because the sweetness of isomalt is relatively low, high-intensity-sweeteners such as aspartame or acesulfame K may be needed to

**Endotherm**—A peak or curve that indicates the amount of energy resulting from a transition from one state to another.

**Dry graining**—Development of a sandy texture caused by recrystallization of an ingredient.

**Heat capacity**—The amount of heat needed to raise the temperature of a substance 1°C.

obtain the desired sweetness level in the final product. Isomalt is synergistic with the sugar alcohols maltitol, lactitol, sorbitol, mannitol, and xylitol. Isomalt has a very low cooling effect, which is desirable for many hard candy applications. It also enhances the flavor of many hard candies (18).

**HSHs.** HSHs can be used as the main base ingredient in hard candy formulations produced by the traditional spinning and forming procedure. HSHs are available in a range of specifications, each produced by a different procedure (see Chapter 3). The high molecular weight HSHs boil at lower temperatures; the low molecular weight HSHs have higher boiling temperatures and require longer boiling times in order to eliminate water. Because high molecular weight HSHs are less sweet, high-intensity sweeteners must be added to formulations in which they are used to obtain the desired sweetness level. The forming temperatures also depend upon the molecular weight of the HSH. Candies made from formulas containing low molecular weight HSHs can be formed at about 70°C, while those made with high molecular weight HSHs form at about 82°C (19).

HSHs also tend to be hygroscopic; the low molecular weight HSHs are more hygroscopic than the high molecular weight HSHs. Care must be taken to process the formula at ambient conditions of about 20°C and 30% relative humidity to inhibit moisture absorption, and final products should be individually wrapped in films that inhibit transmission of water vapor.

During storage, hard candies made with HSHs can develop a defect called *cold flow*, the loss of shape or final form over time. Candies made with low molecular weight HSHs tend to be more susceptible to cold flow than those made with high molecular weight HSHs. High storage temperatures also increase cold flow. To inhibit cold flow, the moisture content of the final products should be <1% (usually about 0.5%; the final moisture content of typical hard candy is about 2–3%), and the viscosity of the formula may need to be modified with gums or polydextrose.

**Maltitol.** Maltitol can be used as the main base ingredient in hard candy formulations. Either the depositing or forming method can be used. Since maltitol can crystallize during storage, a crystal inhibitor must be added to formulations in which it is used. Maltitol has a relatively high level of sweetness, so there is little need for the addition of high-intensity sweeteners. It also has a low cooling effect, which is desirable for many types of hard candies. The processing conditions of maltitol products are similar to those of sucrose- or corn syrup-based formulations, since its solubility and melting points are similar to those of these sugars. The final products must be individually wrapped because they tend to absorb moisture.

**Other sugar alcohols.** Xylitol, mannitol, and lactitol can be used in making transparent hard candies, but because of their inherent properties, they cannot be used alone or as the main base ingredient.

**Cold flow**—Loss of shape or structure of a candy piece during storage over time.

Xylitol has a strong tendency to crystallize and can be used to make recrystallized hard candies by the depositing method. These candies can become very brittle, but the use of HSHs in the formulations decreases this effect (12). Xylitol adds sweetness and has a high cooling effect, which is desirable for mint-flavored candies. Mannitol is a potent crystal inhibitor and can be used for this purpose in formulations that include xylitol. Mannitol is also nonhygroscopic and can be used as a dusting agent on hard candy pieces to prevent them from sticking. Lactitol is also nonhygroscopic and has a low cooling effect. It crystallizes when used at concentrations above 75% (14). When used in combination with HSHs, the final products are less sticky than those made with HSHs alone. Lactitol is desirable for use in low-calorie formulations because it contains 2 calories per gram. However, high-intensity sweeteners may be needed because of its low sweetness level. Hard candies made with lactitol also have improved flavor release (14).

High-intensity sweeteners are used in combination with sugar alcohols when a high level of sweetness is desired. The most commonly used are aspartame and acesulfame K. Aspartame is usually added during the cooling step to minimize losses caused by heat. The more heat-stable encapsulated form can be used during the cooking process. Acesulfame K is very stable when heated and at different pH levels and can be added at various stages during production. It rounds out the flavor of sugar alcohols and enhances the flavors in the final product (4). Polydextrose can also be used as the main bulking agent, with high-intensity sweeteners providing the final product sweetness. Improved forms of polydextrose minimize moisture absorption in the final hard candy products, decreasing stickiness and increasing the product's shelf life (20).

## TABLETED CANDIES

Tableted candies are produced mainly by two methods: wet granulation and direct compaction (Table 4-3). The traditional process, wet granulation, is used to make products that contain nutritive sweeteners. The direct-compaction process was developed for making sugar-free tablets with sorbitol (21) and is clearly much simpler.

In the production of sorbitol tablets, the γ crystalline form, often called tablet grade, is used. Sorbitol does not require much pressure to achieve a high level of hardness in a final product.

**TABLE 4-3.** Typical Tableting Processes

| Method<br>Step | Accomplishment |
| --- | --- |
| Wet-granulation method | |
| Pulverizing | Produces fine particles for smoothness |
| Wet mixing | Adds binder |
| Granulating | Creates large granules or particles |
| Drying | Removes water |
| Sizing | Sets particle size for compaction |
| Blending | Mixes flavor and lubricant |
| Tableting | Gives finished product shape |
| Direct-compaction method | |
| Blending | Mixes ingredients |
| Tableting | Gives finished product shape |

Ambient conditions during processing should be about 20–23°C and <35% relative humidity. Care must be taken in flavor selection because if the flavor is water based, the sorbitol may dissolve, causing the final tablet to become very sticky. Sorbitol tablets can also have a waxy or soapy texture, which is minimized by the addition of xylitol.

Crystalline xylitol can be used in direct-compaction tableting to make compressed mints (22). Friability is a problem with the final product, but it can be minimized with the addition of binders such as gum arabic or sorbitol. The wet-granulation process can also be used to produce xylitol-containing products. Isomalt can be used in the production of tableted candies by direct compaction. The surface of its crystals promotes cohesion. Mannitol softens the final product and is used in the production of chewable tablets. HSHs cannot be used to make tablets because they are liquids. Polydextrose is also directly compressible and is used in combination with high-intensity sweeteners to produce tableted candies.

# Soft Confections

There are many types of soft confections, including chewing gum; fondants and creams; aerated candies; gelled or gummed candies; and chewy candies such as taffy, caramels, nougats, and fudges. The use of nutritive sweeteners in these applications is reviewed elsewhere (1). Although nutritive sweeteners play major functional roles in these products, formulations for high-quality, sugar-free, or reduced-calorie products can be developed. Most soft confections are characterized by their plastic, pliable states, and it is important that they do not stick to the teeth. Nutritive sweeteners used in traditional soft confections can be in solid (crystalline) or liquid (syrup) phases, and as in fondants and chewing gums, both phases may exist simultaneously. Sugar alcohols are prevalent in the production of soft confections because they exist in both of these states, and they are also used as bulk sweeteners. High-intensity sweeteners are used to achieve a high level of sweetness.

## CHEWING GUM

Chewing gum is composed of three phases: a gum base, a crystalline phase, and a liquid phase. The proportions of these phases in a formulation determine the final product's characteristics. For example, more gum base results in a tougher or chewier product. When more of the crystalline phase is present, the product is harder, and when the more of the liquid phase is present, the product is softer. The most prevalent use of alternative sweeteners in chewing gum is in the production of sugar-free varieties. Sugar alcohols are widely used in these products because they can make up the crystalline phase and the liquid phase. HSHs and sorbitol are often used for the liquid phase of the gum. Crystallizable sugar alcohols such as sorbitol (crystalline), xylitol, isomalt, and mannitol are often used for the crystalline phase. These sugar alcohols help to provide texture as well as structure. A small amount of mannitol (<5%) may also be incorporated to inhibit crystallization of other sugar alcohols that may be used. Other sugar alcohols with low solubility, e.g., lactitol and mannitol, are used as dusting agents to inhibit stickiness. The sugar alcohols most commonly used in chewing gum formulations are sorbitol, xylitol, and maltitol.

**Sorbitol.** Sorbitol exists in a liquid, syrup state and a crystalline state, both of which can exist simultaneously in gum formulations. The liquid state helps to keep the gum flexible and chewable and extends shelf life. In chewing gums containing sucrose or corn syrup, the gum base is generally about 20% of the formula. In gums containing sorbitol, the gum base may have to be increased to 30% or more because sorbitol does not provide elasticity (23).

**Xylitol.** Xylitol provides a cooling effect, which contributes to the flavors in mint-type gums. It provides low cohesiveness, great hygroscopicity, and low viscosity, making it difficult to formulate a chewing gum based solely on xylitol. Xylitol used in chewing gum must be in a powder form (particle size <50 μm). Kneading must take place at <55°C so that the xylitol crystals do not melt and cake. The extrusion parameters may need to be adjusted in order to avoid products with *short* textures. The gum base may also need to be increased and an emulsifier such as lecithin added to increase cohesiveness and plasticity (12,22).

**Maltitol.** Maltitol can be used in both the liquid and crystalline phases of chewing gum formulations. Maltitol syrups help to maintain plasticity and thus extend shelf life. They are generally used at levels of 10–40%, depending on the formulation. Maltitol powders are usually incorporated at levels of 45–55% and help to provide texture in the final products.

High-intensity sweeteners are used in combination with the sugar alcohols to provide sweetness. Those commonly used include aspartame, alitame, acesulfame K, sucralose, saccharin, stevioside, and thaumatin. Aspartame can react with certain flavors. Thaumatin masks synthetic tastes, and helps to provide body in the final products. When thaumatin is used, smaller amounts of other high-intensity sweeteners are necessary.

## FONDANTS OR CREMES

The making of traditional fondants or cremes is reviewed elsewhere (1). The final product is a suspension of small sucrose crystals in a liquid syrup phase. Because sugar alcohols can exist in both solid and liquid states, they can be used to produce sugar-free fondants by the same methods used for traditional fondants. Sugar alcohols also work well in these formulations because they do not undergo

**Short**—Pertaining to the texture of a product that breaks apart very easily when bitten.

Maillard browning, resulting in a white final product. In addition, they can act as humectants, providing a smooth, creamy, fine-grained texture and homogeneous, stable final products that do not dry out. Sorbitol is often used in fondants. It is a competent plasticizing agent and humectant and lowers the water activity of the final product, which inhibits microbial activity. High-intensity sweeteners can be incorporated to help obtain the desired sweetness level.

## CARAMELS, TAFFY, NOUGATS, AND FUDGES

In chewy confections (caramels, nougats, and taffies) the sweetener used must exist in a liquid state and must not crystallize. Crystallization causes a grainy texture and a sandy mouthfeel. Likewise, when formulations that include alternative sweeteners are developed, it is important to choose those that will not crystallize during processing or storage. HSHs are often used in these formulations for this reason. They also provide texture and plasticization without causing the product to stick to the teeth. HSHs with longer chain lengths are used to shorten the final product's texture and provide firmness. This is especially useful for taffy formulations. Xylitol provides less body and is used in chewy candies to help shorten textures; it also provides a cooling effect for mint-type products. Sorbitol is used to help plasticize chewy candies. However, if used at high concentrations, it can crystallize in the final product. Maltitol is used as a plasticizing agent, and formulas in which it is used may need higher cooking temperatures and longer pulling times to help achieve the final product texture. Lecithin may also be required to help emulsify the formula ingredients.

Fudge-type products are essentially granulated caramels. Therefore, in the development of sugar-free fudge products, the solubility of the sugar alcohol is of less concern than it is in caramels, taffies, or nougat formulas. Sugar alcohols such as lactitol or mannitol can be used to help achieve the final desired product texture and firmness in combination with HSHs, which help to provide some plasticity.

The flavors of some chewy candies (caramels, toffees, and fudges) depend on Maillard browning. Because the sugar alcohols do not participate in the reaction and can significantly reduce or eliminate it, it may be necessary to increase the amount of milk proteins and lactose present in the other ingredients to ensure that the reaction takes place. Flavors and colors can also be added to achieve the desired final product characteristics.

High-intensity sweeteners, including aspartame, alitame, acesulfame K, sucralose, saccharin, stevioside, and thaumatin, are used to achieve the desired sweetness of the final product. Some factors must be considered when one of these is being chosen. For example, the temperature and pH conditions of the product can affect the stability of some sweeteners. Also, the protein-based high-intensity sweeteners may react with the ingredients in the formula and participate in the Maillard browning reaction.

## GELLED CANDIES

Traditional sweetened gelled or gummed candies contain about 75% sugar composed of 40–50% sucrose and 50–60% corn syrup (24). The sweeteners provide texture and sweetness and inhibit crystallization. Other ingredients include acid, flavor, and a gelling agent (usually starch, pectin, gelatin, or gum such as gum arabic).

Sugar-free products can be produced by using a combination of sugar alcohols and high-intensity sweeteners. The final products are chewy without being sticky and overly sweet. Most products contain a blend of sugar alcohols as well as maltodextrins for additional bulk solids. HSHs and sorbitol are often used in the formulations. HSHs help provide firmness and bulk and do not crystallize, and sorbitol acts as a humectant. An increase in the amount of gelling agent may be necessary in the formulation to make up for the loss of bulk solids that may occur when nutritive sweeteners are replaced by sugar alcohols. High-intensity sweeteners may also be necessary to obtain the desired level of sweetness. Aspartame works well in combination with fruit flavors but can leave a lingering aftertaste (24). It should be added during cooling after the mixture has been cooked so that sweetness is not lost. Acesulfame K provides some bitterness in the final products (24). Sucralose and alitame can be used to achieve clean, sweet flavors. Care must be taken to ensure that the pH of the formula remains below the isoelectric point of gelatin (pH 4.7–5.0) in gelatin-based formulas so that the gelatin does not denature and precipitate. Buffers such as citric acid may be necessary in formulas containing some sugar alcohols. Sanding agents such as xylitol or mannitol can be used for mold release and to prevent products from sticking.

## CHOCOLATES

Sucrose is the main sweetener in traditional chocolate products, and its content can range from 35 to 50%. Chocolate processing with nutritive sweeteners is reviewed elsewhere (1). The general process for traditional chocolate manufacturing is outlined in Figure 4-3. This process can also be used to make chocolates with alternative sweeteners, although slight modifications may be necessary, depending on the alternative sweeteners used. All heat-stable alternative sweeteners

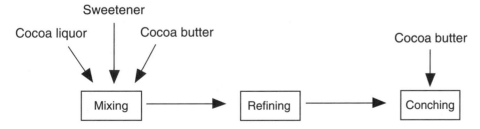

Fig. 4-3. Chocolate-making process.

are added as shown in Figure 4-3. High-intensity sweeteners such as aspartame can be added later in the process to minimize losses caused by heat.

During the refining step, particles in the mix are reduced to about 25–35 µm in diameter, helping to provide a smooth texture and mouthfeel. When sugar alcohols are used as bulk sweeteners, temperatures must be controlled so that they do not exceed the lowest melting point of any sugar alcohol present. Also, if a hygroscopic sugar alcohol is used, the potential moisture absorption must be taken into account.

During *conching,* the mix is homogenized and the fats are dispersed. Cocoa butter can be added at the beginning of the conching step (wet conching) or at the end (dry conching). The mix is heated during conching to about 49–82°C to remove volatiles and moisture and develop flavors. Dark chocolate products are conched at higher temperatures than milk chocolates. The conching temperature for chocolates sweetened with sugar alcohols depends on the lowest melting point of any sugar alcohol used. If the temperature is too high, the sugar alcohol (if not present in an anhydrous form) melts and releases its water, which can then be lost from the system. This loss increases the viscosity of the mix and creates processing difficulties.

Sugar alcohols used in chocolate processing should have high sweetness values (in order to match the sweetness of the traditional product), high melting points, an anhydrous crystalline form, low cooling effects, and low hygroscopicity. In addition to reduced refining and conching temperatures, chocolate products formulated with sugar alcohols may need more cocoa butter or fat than traditional products to help the product melt down.

High-intensity sweeteners can be used in chocolate manufacture to achieve the desired product sweetness level, which may not be attainable with a sugar alcohol alone. Acesulfame K and sucralose can be added during the mixing step because they can withstand the heat of refining and conching. Aspartame can be added at the end of the conching process. Alitame provides clean flavors in chocolate products.

The sugar alcohols commonly used in chocolate products include sorbitol, mannitol, maltitol, lactitol, isomalt, and xylitol.

**Sorbitol.** Sorbitol provides sweetness and a slight cooling effect in chocolates. Since it is very soluble, it can easily be added during the mixing process. The γ crystalline form in a fine grade should be used. If the particles are too small, the final product can appear too dry (25). Because of sorbitol's low melting point, refining and conching temperatures should be reduced. The conching temperature should be 40°C, and the wet conching procedure should be used because sorbitol can recrystallize, resulting in a product with a sandy texture.

**Mannitol.** Mannitol was one of the first sugar alcohols used in chocolate applications because its high melting point and low hygroscopicity allowed the refining and conching steps to remain the same

**Conching**—Slow mixing of a heated chocolate paste to reduce particle size and increase thickness and smoothness.

as those of sucrose-sweetened products (26). However, mannitol's sweetness and solubility characteristics are much lower than those of sucrose. The end products can also have a chalky mouthfeel because of the particle size of the mannitol. Some cooling effect can also be detected.

**Maltitol.** Maltitol is an anhydrous sugar alcohol with a melting point similar to that of sucrose. It can be used in the manufacture of chocolates with no processing changes (26,27). It is highly soluble, which allows easy incorporation during the mixing step. Typical conching temperatures are about 60°C; however, the conching step can be carried out at higher temperatures (e.g., 80°C) to enhance final flavor development (26,27).

**Lactitol.** Lactitol is available commercially in two forms, monohydrate and anhydrous. While either can be used in the making of chocolate products, those made with the anyhydrous form are much easier to process and of higher quality (11). Anhydrous lactitol can be used with no processing changes during the refining and conching steps. Conching can take place at temperatures as high as 80°C, aiding flavor development. Lactitol has good solubility and a low cooling effect. Final products have good mouthfeel (11). It may be necessary to add high-intensity sweeteners to the formula because of lactitol's low sweetness level.

**Isomalt.** When isomalt is used in chocolate products, processing and formulation changes are necessary. Refining and conching temperatures should be about 45°C (not exceeding 50°C) because of its low melting point (15,28). In addition, cocoa butter or additional fats should be added to the formula to help provide good melt-down characteristics.

**Xylitol.** The most notable effect of xylitol in chocolate applications is its cooling effect in the final product, making it useful in the manufacture of chocolate mint-type products. The conching step must be carried out at temperatures up to 55°C. Because of its low viscosity, it may be necessary to add solids (12,22). The final product can become sandy if the relative humidity during storage is >85% (22). Because of its high sweetening power, xylitol can be used as the sole bulk sweetener.

# Troubleshooting

| CHEWING GUM | | |
|---|---|---|
| **Symptom** | **Causes** | **Changes to Make** |
| Tough, chewy | Too much gum base | Decrease gum base content. Increase sugar alcohol content. |
| Dry, brittle; low elasticity | Low moisture content | Check formulation and/or processing conditions. Increase levels of hygroscopic sugar alcohols. Decrease solids content. |
| | Crystallization of sugar alcohol | Decrease level of crystallizable sugar alcohol. Add mannitol. |
| Too sticky | Moisture content too high | Add maltodextrins to increase solids content. Increase boiling temperature and/or time. |
| | Hygroscopic sugar alcohol used | Decrease level of sugar alcohol in formula. Use sugar alcohol with lower hygroscopicity. Use dusting agent (e.g., mannitol or lactitol). |

| CHOCOLATE | | |
|---|---|---|
| **Symptom** | **Causes** | **Changes to Make** |
| Mix too viscous after conching | Sugar alcohol crystals melt and release water, which is lost from the system | Decrease processing temperature to below the melting point of sugar alcohol used. Increase cocoa butter content. Choose a sugar alcohol with a higher melting point. |
| Poor melt-down in mouth | High percentage of sugar alcohol in the formulation | Increase level of fat (e.g., cocoa butter). |
| Mix too thin or does not set properly | Moisture content too high | Check formulation and/or processing conditions. Ensure adequate mixing. Decrease levels of hygroscopic sugar alcohols. Increase solids content. |
| Grainy or gritty texture or crumbly structure | Moisture content too low | Check processing conditions to ensure proper crystal formation. Check particle size and uniformity of sweeteners. |
| | Improper sugar alcohol crystal formation | Check storage conditions for low relative humidity and temperature. |
| | Recrystallization of sorbitol | Use wet conching procedure and conching temperature of 40°C. |

| CARAMELS AND CHEWY CANDIES | | |
|---|---|---|
| **Symptom** | **Causes** | **Changes to Make** |
| Too hard | Low plasticization of formula | Add plasticizing agents (e.g., sorbitol, maltitol, or hydrogenated starch hydrolysates). |
| Lack of color and/or flavor development | Insufficient Maillard browning or caramelization | Add fructose or lactose (if not a sugar-free candy). Increase milk solids content. Increase boiling temperature and/or time. Add colors and/or flavors. |

| Too sticky | Moisture content too high | Add maltodextrins to increase solids. Increase boiling temperature and/or time. |
| | Hygroscopic sugar alcohol used | Decrease level of sugar alcohol in formula. Use sugar alcohol with lower hygroscopicity. Decrease relative humidity and temperature of processing environment (20–23°C, <35% RH). Use dusting agent (e.g., mannitol or lactitol). |
| Gritty or grainy texture | Crystallization of sugar alcohol | Add a crystal inhibitor (e.g., mannitol or hydrogenated starch hydrolysate). Decrease level of crystallizable sugar alcohol. |

## HARD CANDY

| Symptom | Causes | Changes to Make |
| --- | --- | --- |
| Gritty, grainy, or short texture | Crystallization of sugar alcohol | Add a crystal inhibitor (e.g., mannitol). Limit amount of rework. Increase boiling time or temperature to lower moisture content (to 1–2%) and to ensure that crystals dissolve completely. Check quality of incoming ingredients. |
| | Dry graining | Decrease shear and temperature during processing of sorbitol-based candies. |
| Poor or weak flavor | Flavors poorly incorporated because of the structural nature of the matrix | Add emulsifiers. Increase mixing time. Increase flavor level. |
| Cold flow (loss of product shape during storage) | Hydrogenated starch hydrolysate content too high | Decrease level of hydrogenated starch hydrolysate. Increase level of solids (e.g., gums or polydextrose). Make sure final product moisture is <1%. |
| Product too sticky | Moisture content too high | Add maltodextrins to increase solids. Increase boiling temperature and/or time. |
| | Hygroscopic sugar alcohol used | Decrease level of sugar alcohol in formula. Use sugar alcohol with lower hygroscopicity. Decrease relative humidity and temperature of processing environment (20–23°C, <35% RH). Use a dusting agent (e.g., mannitol or lactitol). |

## TABLETED CANDIES

| Symptom | Causes | Changes to Make |
| --- | --- | --- |
| Product too sticky | Sorbitol dissolved in water from water-based flavor | Decrease flavor level. Use flavor that is not water based. |
| | Hygroscopic sugar alcohol used | Decrease level of sugar alcohol in formula. Use sugar alcohol with lower hygroscopicity. |
| Waxy, soapy texture | Sorbitol level too high | Decrease sorbitol level. Add xylitol. |

| GUMMED CANDIES | | |
| --- | --- | --- |
| **Symptom** | **Causes** | **Changes to Make** |
| Product too soft or too sticky | Moisture content too high | Check processing conditions. Increase level of gelling agent or solids. |
| | Hygroscopic sugar alcohol used | Decrease level of sugar alcohol in formula. Use sugar alcohol with lower hygroscopicity. |
| | No release agent in molds | Use a release agent (e.g., mannitol, lactitol, or xylitol). |
| Product too stiff or hard | Moisture content too low | Decrease gelling agent or solids content. |
| | Water too tightly bound | Add plasticizing agent or humectant (e.g., sorbitol). Decrease level of hydrogenated starch hydrolysate. |
| **MARSHMALLOWS AND NOUGATS** | | |
| **Symptom** | **Causes** | **Changes to Make** |
| Product hardens or toughens | Excessive drying | Add humectant (e.g., sorbitol). |
| Coarse and/or gritty texture | Recrystallization of sugar alcohol | Add a crystal inhibitor (e.g., mannitol or hydrogenated starch hydrolysate). |
| Product too dense | Foam breakdown or lack of foam development | Decrease syrup content. Incorporate high-intensity sweeteners with minimum mixing so foam does not collapse. |
| **FONDANTS AND CREMES** | | |
| **Symptom** | **Causes** | **Changes to Make** |
| Product too runny or sticky | Insufficient crystallization | Increase agitation. Increase cooking temperature and/or time. Increase amount of crystallizable form of sugar alcohol. |
| Gritty or grainy texture | Formation of large crystals | Increase agitation. Decrease amount of crystallizable form of sugar alcohol. Add hydrogenated starch hydrolysate. |
| | Crystal growth during storage | Add starch, gelatin, or protein to inhibit crystallization. Decrease amount of crystallizable form of sugar alcohol. |

## References

1. Alexander, R. J. 1998. *Sweeteners: Nutritive.* American Association of Cereal Chemists, St. Paul, MN.
2. Food and Drug Administration. 1980. Confectionery—Use of Non-nutritive Substances as Ingredients. Compliance Policy Guide 7105.01. The Administration, Washington, DC.
3. Hanger, L., von Rymon Lipinski, G., and Nakhost, Z. 1995. Acesulfame-K: Applications in hard candy production. Manufact. Confect. 75(11):75-78.

4. Staniec, N. 1994. Acesulfame K guarantees solubility, stability of sweets. Candy Ind. 159(6):83-85.

5. Mayer, D. G., and Kemper, F. H. 1991. *Acesulfame-K*. Marcel Dekker, New York.

6. NutraSweet Kelco. 1997. Confections: Applications Overview. Tech. Bull. 5212. NutraSweet Kelco, Chicago.

7. Nabors, L. 1990. Intense sweeteners: Acesulfame-K, alitame, aspartame, saccharin, sucralose. Manufact. Confect. 70(11):65-68.

8. Bakal, A. 1997. A satisfyingly sweet overview. Prep. Foods 166(3):47-50.

9. Anonymous. 1996. Thaumatin—The sweetest substance known to man has a wide range of food applications. Food Tech. 50:74-75.

10. Ross, R. 1990. Bulk ingredients: Sugar alcohols and alternative sweeteners in confections. Manufact. Confect. 70(11):49-54.

11. Olinger, P. 1995. Lactitol: Its use in chocolate. Xylitol as a sanding medium. Manufact. Confect. 75(11):92-95.

12. Pepper, T., and Olinger, P. 1988. Xylitol in sugar-free confections. Food Tech. 42(10):98-106.

13. Shinsanto, E. 1996. Confectionery ingredient update. Cereal Foods World 41:372-375.

14. Mesters, P. 1995. Lactitol, bulk sweetener for sugar free and reduced calorie hard candy. Manufact. Confect. 75(11):61-63.

15. Irwin, W. E. 1990. Reduced calorie bulk ingredients: Isomalt. Manufact. Confect. 70(11):55-60.

16. Klacik, K. 1989. Continuous production of sugar free hard candies. Manufact. Confect. 69(8):61-67.

17. Klacik, K. 1990. Applications in confectionery: Sugarless hard candy technology review. Manufact. Confect. 70(11):69-76.

18. Fritzsching, B. 1995. Isomalt in hard candy applications. Manufact. Confect. 75(11):65-73.

19. Raleigh, W. 1995. HSH as a bulking agent in confections. Manufact. Confect. 75(11):57-59.

20. Kopchik, F. M. 1990. Reduced calorie bulk ingredients: Polydextrose and polydextrose II. Manufact. Confect. 70(11):61-63.

21. Vink, W. 1990. Applications in confectionery: Tableted confections. Manufact. Confect. 70(11):77-80.

22. Hyvonen, L., Koivistoinen, P., and Voirol, F. 1982. Food technological evaluation of xylitol. Adv. Food Res. 28:373-403.

23. Marie, S., and Piggott, J. R. 1991. *Handbook of Sweeteners*. AVI, New York.

24. Burg, J. S. 1998. Generating yummy gummies. Food Prod. Design, May, pp. 121-146.

25. Grenby, T. H., Parker, K. J., and Lindley, M. G. 1983. *Developments in Sweeteners, Vol. 2*. Applied Science Publishers, New York.

26. Happel, B. L. 1995. Crystalline maltitol in the manufacture of chocolate. Manufact. Confect. 75(11):96-99.

27. Rapaille, A., Gonze, M., and Van der Schueren, F. 1995. Formulating sugar-free chocolate products with maltitol. Manufact. Confect. 49(7):51-52, 54.

28. Olinger, P. M. 1994. New options for sucrose-free chocolate. Manufact. Confect. 74(5):77-84.

# Bakery and Other Grain-Based Applications

Most often, alternative sweeteners are used to replace nutritive sweeteners in baked goods and other grain-based products in order to create foods with fewer calories. Product development may also be focused on creating baked goods that taste sweet but do not raise blood glucose levels as high as those containing nutritive sweeteners such as sucrose and glucose.

## Product Characteristics

Traditional sweeteners are responsible for many of the attributes of baked goods and other grain-based applications such as extruded cereals and snacks and granola bars. Replacing all or even a portion of these nutritive sweeteners with alternative sweeteners may cause changes in these attributes. The main functions of nutritive sweeteners and their effects in various applications are reviewed fully elsewhere (1). A brief discussion of how nutritive and alternative sweeteners affect certain product attributes is included here.

### NUTRITIVE SWEETENERS

**Sweetness and flavor.** Nutritive sweeteners impart sweetness and contribute to other flavors that result from Maillard browning or *caramelization*. Some sweeteners, such as honey and maple syrup, have unique flavors of their own, which are also imparted to products.

**Brown color formation.** Browning results from Maillard browning reactions between reducing sugars and amino acids or proteins and from caramelization. The colors of some sweeteners (e.g., honey, maple syrup, and refiner's syrups) also contribute to the color of the final product.

**Structure.** Nutritive sweeteners inhibit starch *gelatinization* and protein coagulation during baking, imparting structure to cakes, crispness and snap to cookies, and cohesiveness to granola-type products.

**Texture.** The hygroscopic nature of nutritive sweeteners aids in maintaining crumb softness, keeping granola products pliable and not too hard, and providing a moist and tender mouthfeel.

**Caramelization**—A series of reactions that sucrose undergoes when heated, resulting in final reaction products such as brown pigments and caramel flavors.

**Gelatinization**—Collapse (disruption) of molecular orders within starch granules manifested by irreversible changes in properties such as granular swelling, native crystalline melting, loss of birefringence, and starch solubilization.

**Appearance.** Nutritive sweeteners influence the surface cracking of cookies, affect the finish of frostings and icings, and help adhere particulates to the surfaces of products.

Since traditional sweeteners not only add sweetness but also affect a variety of product characteristics, the product developer must carefully consider the attributes of the product and how the removal or partial replacement of the sweetening system will affect those attributes. It may be necessary to find other ways to achieve these characteristics.

## ALTERNATIVE SWEETENERS

**Sweetness, flavor, and color.** Several high-intensity sweeteners can be used to provide sweetness to baked goods and other grain-based products. Aspartame and thaumatin, however, cannot withstand baking temperatures and do not contribute sweetness to the final products. An encapsulated form of aspartame has been developed that is more heat stable and better able to withstand baking temperatures as well as a broad range of pH levels.

Sugar alcohols can also be used to provide sweetness in bakery applications. Sorbitol, xylitol, and maltitol have comparatively high relative sweetness values and may be used in replacement formulations at levels near or equal to that of sucrose. However, it may be necessary to include high-intensity sweeteners in formulations in which lactitol, isomalt, mannitol, and hydrogenated starch hydrolysates (HSHs) are used.

Some alternative sweeteners may affect the flavor of baked goods and other grain-based applications. For example, aspartame works very well in fruit-based systems and is known to enhance fruit flavors while masking the metallic or bitter notes of saccharin. Some sugar alcohols, particularly xylitol, mannitol, and sorbitol, have a cooling effect on the tongue and may impart a cooling sensation to the final product. Isomalt has a low cooling effect and is often used in baked products.

Most alternative sweeteners do not undergo Maillard browning, and none undergoes caramelization. Sweeteners that do participate in Maillard browning, i.e., aspartame, alitame, thaumatin, and glycyrrhizin, are those that contain amino acids. Since these are high-intensity sweeteners, their levels in baked goods applications are usually very low and their contribution to the reaction is limited. Thus, it may be necessary to add flavors and colors to achieve the desired reaction flavor and browning in the final product. Because there may be a loss of sweetness as a result of the reaction, it may be necessary to increase the amount of sweetener in the formula or add it during a separate processing step.

**Structure.** High-intensity sweeteners and sugar alcohols cannot inhibit starch gelatinization and protein coagulation, mainly because they are present in such low concentrations, and bulking agents are required to achieve structure in baked goods in which they are used. Sugar alcohols, which can be used in greater amounts than high-intensity sweeteners, cannot provide the structure achieved with sucrose and other nutritive sweeteners because, although they are hygroscopic, they do not hydrate (i.e., bind water) to the extent that nutritive sweeteners do.

Crispness and snap in baked goods applications depend on the crystallization or formation of a *glass* structure by nutritive sweeteners. Crispness is also related to the hardness of a product. It is important that nonhygroscopic ingredients be used so that the final product does not absorb moisture over time and become soggy. Because they are hygroscopic, sorbitol, maltitol, and xylitol should be used sparingly or avoided in products in which crispness is desired.

**Softness.** The hygroscopic nature of sorbitol, maltitol, and xylitol helps to keep the crumb of products soft and granola products pliable and not too hard. Sorbitol is often used in reduced-fat and reduced-sugar cake products to maintain crumb softness and moist mouthfeel. These sugar alcohols can also help when cohesion or adhesion of particles to a surface is necessary.

**Appearance.** Alternative sweeteners can affect appearance in a variety of ways. How they influence the appearance of particular products is discussed in detail later in this chapter.

## Processing Characteristics

In addition to its final characteristics, a product's processing conditions must be evaluated when an alternative sweetener or sweetening system is being chosen. Some alternative sweeteners cannot withstand baking temperatures and may degrade to compounds that are no longer sweet. Some may participate in the browning reaction that occurs with heat but may not be able to provide the brown color at their levels of usage, and others may not participate at all. Table 5.1 lists the major alternative sweeteners and how they influence or participate in the functionalities of baked goods.

Heat stability is one of the most important characteristics of an alternative sweetener used in baked goods. Most high-intensity alternative sweeteners can withstand heat and provide sweetness after baking. Alitame has shown some losses during baking of particular products, but >80% is retained in most baked goods (2). Acesulfame K exhibits excellent heat stability in baked goods such as cookies and cakes with recovery rates of 98–100% (3). Sucralose is also heat stable, and performance tests have shown 100% recovery in baked goods such as cakes, cookies, and graham crackers (4). Aspartame is not heat stable but is available in a more stable encapsulated form. The recovery rates of encapsulated aspartame after baking in cookies and cakes are reportedly 94.6 and 79%, respectively. Although the natural high-intensity sweeteners glycyrrhizin and stevioside are heat stable, they

**Glass**—Containing no crystallinity.

TABLE 5-1. Properties of Alternative Sweeteners in Bakery Applications

| Alternative Sweetener | Withstands Baking Temperatures | Participates in Maillard Browning[a] | Delays Starch Gelatinization[b] | Provides Cohesiveness and/or Crumb Softness |
|---|---|---|---|---|
| High-intensity sweeteners | | | | |
| Synthetic | | | | |
| Saccharin | Y | N | N | N |
| Cyclamate | Y | N | N | N |
| Aspartame | . . .[c] | Y[d] | N | N |
| Alitame | Y | Y[d] | N | N |
| Acesulfame K | Y | N | N | N |
| Sucralose | Y | N | N | N |
| Natural | | | | |
| Glycyrrhizin | Y | Y[d] | N | N |
| Thaumatin | N | Y[d] | N | N |
| Stevioside | Y | Y | N | N |
| Sugar alcohols | | | | |
| Sorbitol | Y | N | N | N |
| Mannitol | Y | N | N | Y |
| Maltitol | Y | N | N | Y |
| Lactitol | Y | N | N | Y |
| Isomalt | Y | N | N | Y |
| Hydrogenated starch hydrolysates | Y | N | N | Y |
| Xylitol | Y | N | N | Y |

[a] None of the alternative sweeteners listed participates in caramelization.

[b] At typical usage levels.

[c] A more heat-stable, encapsulated form is available.

[d] Can participate in the Maillard browning reaction, but at typical usage levels, does not usually impart a brown color, and sweetness is lost after reaction.

are not often used in baked goods because they impart off-flavors to products. All the sugar alcohols are very heat stable and can withstand baking conditions.

## Hard Wheat Products

In general, hard wheat products are those in which a *gluten* structure is developed by kneading the wheat flour proteins in the presence of water. Popular hard wheat products include yeast-raised breads, rolls, bagels, and sweet rolls. The typical concentration of traditional sweeteners in these products is 0–8%, but it can be as high as 10–15% in sweet-dough products. Nutritive sweeteners in hard wheat products provide a source of fermentable carbohydrate for the yeast. The fermentation process produces gas, which causes the product to

**Gluten**—The resultant product of mixing the wheat proteins gliadin and glutenin in the presence of water.

rise and form an air cell structure. Fermentation also creates reducing sugars such as glucose and fructose, which participate in Maillard browning and caramelization reactions and give the product its brown crust colors. Depending on the desired final product, additional sweeteners may be added to enhance the brown color formation. Nutritive sweeteners also affect the texture of the product because their hydration results in products that are sometimes more dense. This is especially true for sweet-dough products, in which the concentration of sweetener is greater.

Alternative sweeteners are not often used to replace traditional sweeteners in products such as breads and rolls for two reasons. First, because nutritive sweeteners are used at such low levels in these products, replacing them with alternative sweeteners does not have a significant effect on their calorie content. Instead, calories are usually reduced by using less fat, replacing flour with a fiber source, adding emulsifiers and vital wheat gluten, and increasing the moisture contents of final products (5). Second, nutritive sweeteners serve specific functions in these products, for example, in the fermentation stages of the yeast. Yeasts utilize starch as a food source but preferentially utilize readily available, easily fermentable sources such as glucose or sucrose. The sugar alcohols xylitol, mannitol, and sorbitol inhibit yeast activity, and the product may not fully proof or rise to the extent desired. It may be necessary to add a fermentable carbohydrate source (such as sucrose), add enzymes to aid in the breakdown of starch to provide fermentable carbohydrates, or modify expectations of the final product. In most cases, sufficient amounts of reducing sugars are produced from the fermentation of starch so that Maillard browning and caramelization reactions can be controlled by temperature. The addition of enzymes to break down starch to simple sugars could also aid in the browning processes.

In sweet-dough products, to which nutritive sweeteners are added at higher levels for the purpose of sweetening, substitution with an alternative sweetener has a more profound effect. The effects on fermentation and brown color crust formation are the same as for breads and rolls. However, sweet-dough products are moist and soft because of their higher sugar levels, which inhibit gluten development. Thus, the partial or full replacement of the sugars can result in a drier, tougher product. Hygroscopic agents, such as sugar alcohols, can be added to help increase moistness. *Gums*, cellulose, or starches can also be added to help bind the moisture. To reduce toughness, plasticizing agents can be incorporated, either by increasing the fat content or, if calories are a concern, by adding emulsifiers.

## Soft Wheat Products

Familiar soft wheat baked products include cakes, cookies, brownies, and chemically leavened products such as muffins, quick breads, pancakes, and waffles. The typical amounts of nutritive sweeteners

**Gum**—Water-soluble or modified polysaccharide used for thickening and water binding.

**TABLE 5-2.** Typical Concentrations of Nutritive Sweeteners in Soft Wheat Products

| Product Category | Sweetener Concentration (%) |
|---|---|
| Cakes | 25–30 |
| Cookies | 20–40 |
| Brownies | 20–40 |
| Quick breads and muffins | 25–30 |
| Pancakes and waffles | 5–10 |

found in these products are shown in Table 5-2. Within these product categories, there are many types or varieties. Cakes can range from angel food to devil's food. Cookies can range from crisp and hard to soft and chewy. Brownies can range from fudgelike to cakelike. Muffin types include corn, bran, and those based on fruits such as blueberry or apple.

One of the main functions of nutritive sweeteners in these products is to provide sweetness. When replacing nutritive with alternative sweeteners, the product developer's objective is usually

**TABLE 5-3.** Characteristics Imparted by Nutritive Sweeteners to Soft Wheat Baked Goods

| Product Category | Characteristic[a] | Process |
|---|---|---|
| Cakes | Fine air cell size | Contribute to creaming |
| | Crumb structure | Inhibit starch gelatinization and protein denaturation |
| | Moist, tender crumb | Act as humectants |
| | Shelf life | Inhibit microbial spoilage and drying |
| Cookies | Hardness, crispness | Inhibit starch gelatinization; melt and recrystallize, forming a hard, glasslike structure |
| | Softness, chewiness | Act as humectants (brown sugar, honey) |
| | Crumb structure | Contribute to creaming |
| | Spread | Melt to create a more fluid dough |
| | Surface cracking | Recrystallizes and dries the surface (sucrose) |
| | Browning | Participate in Maillard browning and caramelization reactions and contribute their own inherent colors |
| | Shelf life | Inhibit microbial spoilage and drying of chewy products |
| Brownies | Dense, heavy, fudgelike texture | Act as humectants; inhibit starch gelatinization and protein denaturation |
| | Cakelike texture | Set structure |
| | Shelf life | Inhibit microbial spoilage and drying of fudgelike products |
| Quick breads, muffins, pancakes, waffles, and other chemically leavened products | Structure | Inhibit starch gelatinization and protein denaturation |
| | Very moist, tender crumb | Act as humectants |
| | Browning | Participate in Maillard browning and caramelization reactions and contribute their own inherent colors |
| | Shelf life | Inhibit microbial spoilage and drying |

[a] Sweetness is a major characteristic imparted for all categories.

to match the original product's sweetness profile. The alternative sweetener must also be able to withstand the processing conditions of pH and temperature without contributing off-flavors such as metallic or bitter notes. Several alternative sweeteners, including acesulfame K, alitame, aspartame (the encapsulated form), cyclamate, sucralose, and the sugar alcohols, meet these requirements. Others, such as saccharin or glycyrrhizin, can also be used. However, special formulations may be necessary to mask off-flavors. The alternative sweetener chosen depends on the flavor profile desired for the final product.

Nutritive sweeteners serve various functions, and different sweeteners produce different results within a product category. For example, sucrose yields a crisp cookie product, while the use of brown sugar in the same formulation results in a cookie that is softer and more chewy. The functions of nutritive sweeteners and how they influence soft wheat products are reviewed elsewhere (1). In general, nutritive sweeteners provide sweetness, tender crumb, moistness, crispness, chewiness, shelf life, batter viscosity, dough cohesiveness, and structure-setting properties. The specific properties imparted by nutritive sweeteners in the major soft wheat product categories are outlined in Table 5-3. An ideal alternative sweetener would provide most of these characteristics including bulk and structure, have few or no calories, be soluble, tolerate the varying processing conditions of heat and pH, be safe to consume, bind water or reduce water activity, add viscosity, incorporate and retain air, and influence starch gelatinization and protein *denaturation* temperatures. No single alternative sweetener with all these properties currently exists. Replacing nutritive with alternative sweeteners thus provides a challenge for the product developer, and multicomponent (multi-ingredient) approaches are necessary to achieve the desired final product attributes.

## CAKES

Nutritive sweeteners provide structure to cakes by participating in *creaming,* the process by which air is incorporated into the shortening, resulting in air cells in the final product. Nutritive sweeteners also provide bulk, batter viscosity, and proper setting of the crumb by delaying both starch gelatinization and protein denaturation. They

**Denaturation**—The process that proteins undergo when subjected to certain chemical or physical treatments (e.g., heating) that cause disruption of the noncovalent bonds that maintain their secondary and tertiary structure, resulting in profound changes in functional properties.

**Creaming**—The incorporation of air by rapidly mixing a crystalline substance into a solid substance (e.g., sugar into butter).

### Box 5-1. Polydextrose

Polydextrose is a polymer of glucose, sorbitol, and citric acid (89:10:1) available commercially in liquid and powder forms. It contains 1 calorie per gram and thus can be used to add bulk and solids to low-calorie foods. It improves the texture of many foods, and in dry mixes, it increases flowability, allows uniform dispersion, and decreases lumping. Because it is slightly acidic, the pH of the formulation should be monitored and adjusted if necessary.

influence crumb characteristics (moistness and tenderness) and shelf life. Sucrose, the main sweetener in cakes, is used at levels of about 25–30%, and high-intensity sweeteners are typically used in cake formulations at 0.1–2%, depending on the sweetener. Thus, the full or partial replacement of sucrose by a high-intensity sweetener affects all these properties.

**Structure.** Sucrose binds water and creates bulk in cake systems. When sucrose is removed from the formula, the water remains available, causing early onset of starch gelatinization and protein denaturation and the ultimate failure of the structure (Fig. 5-1). Agents such as maltodextrins and granular sugar alcohols can be used during creaming to add bulk, and the addition of emulsifiers helps in the incorporation and retention of air during this step. One of the most common and effective ways to maintain bulk and batter viscosity in cakes is to add polydextrose, which both binds water to build viscosity and provides bulk solids, helping to build and set the final structure. Because polydextrose can affect the pH of the formulation, however, the leavening system may need to be adjusted by manipulating the sodium bicarbonate levels. The typical level of polydextrose in cakes is 7–15% by weight. If too much polydextrose is used, a heavy cake with a syrupy mouthfeel and bitter aftertaste can result (6). Also, shrinkage can occur, affecting the volume of the final product. In dry mix cake formulations, polydextrose aids flowability and the uniform dispersion of the dry ingredients and can also help prevent lumping of the dry ingredients in the package over time (5). Another bulking agent, powdered cellulose, has also shown positive results (7). Unlike polydextrose, powdered cellulose is an insoluble bulking agent. Sugar alcohols can also be used to provide bulk and viscosity. In some formulations, they can be used alone to replace sucrose without the need for other bulking agents. Frye and Setser (8) have reviewed the use of six bulking agents in cake formulations: polydextrose, maltodextrin, sorbitol, lactitol, isomalt, and an HSH. Their research shows that a puffed appearance and air pocket formation do not occur when maltodextrin and polydextrose are used, which they attribute to the high batter viscosities of the formulations.

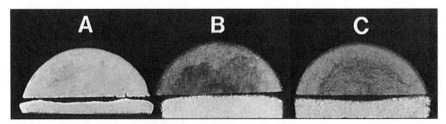

Fig. 5-1. Comparison of volume and relative crumb structure in three yellow cake formulations. **A,** sugar-free, no bulking agent; **B,** control (normal sugar content); and **C,** sugar-free with polydextrose and increased leavening. (Reprinted from L. L. Hood and L. A. Campbell, 1990, Developing reduced calorie bakery products with sucralose, Cereal Foods Word 35:1171-1172, 1177-1182)

**Crumb characteristics.** To help maintain crumb tenderness and moistness, a sugar alcohol such as sorbitol, mannitol, or xylitol can be added. Other humectants, such as water-binding starches and gums, can also be used. Cakes in which lactitol is used exhibit the same shelf life and eating qualities as control cakes with sucrose. Maltitol and HSHs can replace corn syrup in cakes without negatively affecting the properties in the system. Polydextrose also improves crumb characteristics, but gummy textures have been noted (5).

**Shelf life.** In addition to their effects on crumb characteristics, humectants improve the shelf life of a product by binding and retaining water. This keeps the product moist and makes the water less available to microorganisms for growth. If the water content is increased in the formulation to aid mouthfeel, proper shelf life studies should be conducted to determine whether preservatives and modified-atmosphere packaging are needed.

## COOKIES

As in cakes, nutritive sweeteners provide structure to cookies by participating in creaming, allowing for the incorporation of air into the shortening and resulting in air cells in the final product. The effects of sucrose reduction or replacement on creaming can be resolved as discussed above. Nutritive sweeteners also affect cookie texture: some produce hard, crisp products and others soft, chewy products. Sweeteners also influence the spread, surface cracking, and brown color formation of the final product. The typical concentration of high-intensity sweeteners in cookie formulations is 0.5–2%. Since the typical nutritive sweetener content of cookies is 20–40%, challenges in product development occur.

**Texture.** Once sucrose or other traditional sweeteners are removed from a cookie formulation, the bulk is lost and solids must be replaced with bulking agents. Adding them at the creaming stage helps reduce lumping in the dough and decreases the possibility of a gummy texture (9). However, most bulking agents also bind water, creating problems with cookies that are meant to be crisp and hard and have snap. This is less of an issue with soft, chewy cookies, and bulking agents such as polydextrose, cellulose powders, fibers, gums, and maltodextrins can be used with good results (6). However, greater hardness and fracturability have been observed in cookies that contain polydextrose (6). To create a truly hard, crisp texture, some sucrose must be present in order for recrystallization to take place, resulting in the formation of a glass structure. Sugar alcohols with low hygroscopicity (i.e., mannitol, isomalt, and lactitol) also aid in achieving crispness (5).

**Appearance.** When traditional sweeteners melt during baking, the dough becomes less viscous and flows outward. Reduction in spread is one of the most notable results of replacing nutritive sweeteners. Adding bulking agents does not solve the problem, since most bind water, resulting in a more viscous dough with less spread during baking. Polydextrose increases the spread of certain cookie formulations while decreasing dough cohesiveness. Sugar alcohols can also be used (6), and if the fat content is not of primary concern in the final product, it can be increased to help improve spread. However, it may be necessary to retain some nutritive sweeteners in the formula to allow the spreading process to occur.

The cracking that occurs on the cookie surface results from the recrystallization of sucrose and the drying of the surface. Again, these processes are inhibited when the added bulking agents bind water. Reducing the moisture level in the formula can improve cracking but can also reduce the dough-handling quality, inhibit spread, and result in a dry, brittle product. If surface cracking is a necessary characteristic of the product, it may be necessary to retain some sucrose in the formula.

When nutritive sweeteners are removed, the Maillard browning and caramelization reactions are inhibited, resulting in a decrease in brown color formation. The addition of maltodextrins can help. Natural or artificial colors may also improve the product's appearance.

## BROWNIES

Development issues for reduced-sugar, sugar-free, or low-calorie brownies are much the same as those for cake products, especially if the final product is a cakelike brownie. If the final product is a fudge-like brownie, formula development focuses on maintaining moisture, which can be achieved by using sugar alcohols or increasing bulking agent and water contents.

## CHEMICALLY LEAVENED PRODUCTS

Chemically leavened products include quick breads, muffins, pancakes, and waffles. Again, many of the development issues involved in cake making also apply to these products. However, since these products depend on the leavening system for the incorporation of air, creaming is not a consideration. Because bulking agents, such as polydextrose, can alter the pH, care must be taken to ensure that the pH of the batter is the same as that of the original formulation so that the leavening system functions properly. Adjustments can be made by manipulating the levels of sodium bicarbonate. More liquids may be needed to maintain the consistency of the batter. Adding more eggs can help with aeration and the structure of the final product. Sugar alcohols are effective in maintaining the tender, moist crumb (especially in quick breads and muffins) (6). The browning of pancakes and waffles depends on the caramelization reactions that take place when the batter touches the cooking surface. Maltodextrins can aid in this process, and fructose can help in products that are not sugar free.

# Topical Applications

In general, replacing nutritive sweeteners presents less of a development challenge in topical applications such as frostings, icings, and fillings than in baked goods. These products are semisolid and have a plastic flow, so bulking agents have less of an effect on the final product. Topical dustings of sweeteners are difficult to replace, because most granular high-intensity sweeteners are too intense to be used alone and must be diluted with an agent such as polydextrose. However, these combinations do not provide the clear, crystalline appearance of sucrose crystals. Other granular alternative sweeteners such as sugar alcohols are also unacceptable because of their cooling effect on the tongue, cloudy appearance, grainy mouthfeel, or low sweetness levels.

## FROSTINGS

Frostings are typically prepared by creaming the shortening with sugar and then adding colors, emulsifiers, flavors, or other ingredients such as cocoa. The final product should be creamy and dissolve easily on the tongue. High-intensity sweeteners that are approved for use can replace sucrose in frosting applications. Crystalline sugar alcohols, which easily dissolve on the tongue, can also be used. Sorbitol, xylitol, and lactitol can be used but may have a cooling effect, depending upon their usage levels. The heat stability of the sweetener is not a concern. As in baked goods, the bulk solids must be replaced. Starches and celluloses have been used successfully for this purpose in frosting applications. A granular agent or other ingredient must be added to the creaming step to incorporate air and make the frosting light and fluffy.

Nutritive sweeteners act as humectants in frostings and keep them soft and moist. One of the problems encountered with reformulated frostings is that they dry out, a defect referred to as *case hardening*. Using hygroscopic sugar alcohols (e.g., sorbitol, xylitol, and maltitol) can help to prevent this. Moisture migration can also be a concern. The final water activity values of the cake and the frosting may be very different from those of the original formulas, and moisture may migrate from the lower to the higher water activity system. If the water activity of the cake is lower than that of the frosting, the frosting may dry out. If the water activity of the frosting is lower than that of the cake, the frosting may become overly glossy and even slide off the cake. To avert these problems, the water activity of both products should be examined and possibly adjusted. Glycerin, sorbitol, or additives such as water-binding starches can be used for this purpose.

## ICINGS

Unlike frostings, icings are usually boiled. They are generally thinner than frostings, so less bulking agent is necessary, and their final

**Case hardening**—The formation of a hardened outer shell or skin over a softer or more liquid entity.

appearance can be matte, glossy, or frosted. The solubility of alternative sweeteners is less of a concern in icings than in other applications because they can be dissolved during the boiling step and then distributed throughout the system's matrix. A glossy appearance can be achieved with fructose or hygroscopic sugar alcohols (e.g., sorbitol, xylitol, and maltitol), which work well to attract water to the surface of the icing. However, a frosted appearance is more difficult to attain because it results from the recrystallization of sucrose. Thus, it may not be possible to replace all the sucrose in the formula. The whiteness of most bulking agents may provide this white, frosted look as well, but icings may look cloudy or nonuniform, depending on the final product.

## FILLINGS

The term "fillings" is used here to refer to the types of products developed for foods such as pies and tarts. Reducing the nutritive sweetener content of these products is less of a development challenge than in some other applications because the bulk provided by nutritive sweeteners can be replaced with a *hydrocolloid* system that includes a high-intensity sweetener. Fillings are usually cooked, so starches are most often used as the thickening agents. Alternative sweeteners such as alitame, encapsulated aspartame, and sucralose, which are stable when heated, work well in these applications.

# Ready-to-Eat Cereals and Granola Products

Nutritive sweeteners perform several functions in ready-to-eat cereals and granola products. They provide flavor and color and are used as processing aids, in coating applications, and for adhesion (1). Cereal products are usually produced in batches in large vat cookers or in continuous single- or twin-screw extruders. Nutritive sweeteners can be added during any of the various unit operations (dry mix blending, cooking/extrusion, or coating/enrobing).

The problems that arise with the replacement of nutritive sweeteners in uncoated cereal products involve the formation of flavors, colors, and textures. Replacing the solids lost with the removal of sucrose is less of an issue, since the final volume of the cereal pieces is achieved by the puffing/toasting process. Solids can be replaced with starches and fibers, and the lubricating effect that sucrose provides during processing can be reproduced by varying the amount of water or emulsifier used in the formula. The main problem encountered in replacing traditional sweeteners in uncoated cereal pieces is that the high-intensity alternative sweeteners cannot withstand the processing conditions of batch cooking or extrusion. In addition, the important flavor- and color-development reactions in which traditional sweeteners participate during processing are very difficult to reproduce with natural or artificial colors or flavors, because, like sweeteners, they cannot withstand the processing conditions.

### Typical Creme Filling Formula

| Ingredient | Content (%) |
|---|---|
| Maltitol | 70.3 |
| Vanilla flavor | 0.3 |
| Salt | 0.2 |
| Icing shortening | 29.18 |
| Lecithin | 0.02 |

### Typical Fruit Filling Formula

| Ingredient | Content (%) |
|---|---|
| Water | 71 |
| Starch | 6.8 |
| Dehydrated apples | 7 |
| Brown sugar | 15 |
| Cinnamon | 0.1 |
| Salt | 0.07 |
| High-intensity sweetener | 0.03 |

**Hydrocolloid**—Gum; water-soluble or modified polysaccharide used for thickening and water binding.

Coating applications usually involve the formulation of a boiled syrup containing sucrose or other nutritive sweeteners (e.g., corn syrups), which provide bulk solids and viscosity. The cereal or granola pieces are enrobed with the syrup and then dried to product specifications. Alternative sweeteners are difficult to use in these applications. If a clear final coating is desired, bulking agents such as fibers, starches, or celluloses cannot be used. Gums are also difficult to use in some formulations because of the mouthfeel that they impart. Sugar alcohols with low hygroscopicity (mannitol, isomalt, or lactitol) can be used, but their solubility in solution can cause problems in some formulations. Hygroscopic sugar alcohols can be used for adhesion purposes (e.g., in granola products), but in cereal applications, they cause pieces to agglomerate over time.

## Troubleshooting

| BAKED GOODS—GENERAL | | |
|---|---|---|
| **Symptom** | **Causes** | **Changes to Make** |
| Very low batter viscosity or sticky dough | Water level too high | Check calculation of water content. Be sure moisture or water content of sweetener is considered, and adjust addition of free water accordingly.<br>Add a bulking agent (e.g., carbohydrate polymers, fiber, gum, or polydextrose). |
| | Level of hygroscopic agents (e.g., sugar alcohols) too high | Reduce sugar alcohol content.<br>Use a sugar alcohol with low hygroscopicity (e.g., lactitol or isomalt). |
| Poor texture of final product | Poor creaming | Use granular alternative sweeteners or sugar alcohols.<br>Add eggs or emulsifier to improve structure and aeration. |
| | Loss of moistness, tender crumb, or structure | Add a humectant (e.g., sugar alcohol, fibers, or gums).<br>Increase liquid content. |
| | Loss of structure | Add a bulking agent (e.g., carbohydrate polymers, fiber, gum, or polydextrose).<br>Add eggs or emulsifier to improve structure and aeration. |
| Low or no brown color formation | Not enough reducing sugars present to participate in Maillard browning or caramelization reactions | Add fructose or a maltodextrin with a higher dextrose equivalent.<br>Increase baking time and/or temperature. |
| Low or no sweetness | Degradation of alternative sweetener caused by pH or heat | Choose an alternative sweetener that remains stable under processing conditions used. |
| Off-flavors or odors | Degradation of alternative sweetener or reaction with other ingredients | Check quality of incoming ingredients.<br>Choose an alternative sweetener that remains stable under processing conditions used. |
| Rapid drying and staling of final product | Inadequate water absorption and retention | Add a humectant (e.g., sugar alcohol, fibers, or gums).<br>Add preservatives.<br>Use modified-atmosphere packaging. |

## YEAST-RAISED PRODUCTS

| Symptom | Causes | Changes to Make |
|---|---|---|
| Low volume, long proof time, pale crust, no break and shred | Insufficient fermentation and gas production | Add a nutritive sweetener. Increase fermentation by increasing time, temperature, or enzymatic activity. |
| Small or no cell structure and high density | Yeast action and growth inhibited by sugar alcohols | Remove sugar alcohols. |
| Crust too thick | Excessive fermentation | Reduce fermentation by decreasing time, temperature, or enzymatic activity. |
| Excessive volume with large, nonuniform cell structure or open crumb grain | Excessive fermentation and gas production | Reduce fermentation by decreasing time, temperature, or enzymatic activity. |

## SWEET GOODS

| Symptom | Causes | Changes to Make |
|---|---|---|
| Thick, leathery crust | Too much bulking agent added | Decrease level of bulking agent. Add fat or emulsifier. |
| Tough, dry crumb | Overdevelopment of gluten | Add nutritive sweetener to inhibit development of gluten. Decrease mixing time. |
|  | Low plasticization of dough | Add plasticizing agent (e.g., fat, sugar alcohol, or emulsifier). |
| Excessive batter viscosity, usually resulting in small, sticky, gummy crumb structure and high-density products | Too much bulking agent added | Decrease level of bulking agent. Increase fat or liquid levels. Add emulsifier. |

## CAKES

| Symptom | Causes | Changes to Make |
|---|---|---|
| Low volume | Little or no aeration during creaming | Use an alternative sweetener with larger granules. Add emulsifiers. |
| Gummy crumb, heavy or syrupy mouthfeel | Too much bulking agent added | Decrease level of bulking agent (especially polydextrose). |
| Collapsed structure | Early onset of starch gelatinization and protein coagulation | Increase level of bulking agent. |
|  | Improper pH balance for leavening system | Adjust pH with sodium bicarbonate (especially if polydextrose was used). |
|  | Formula imbalance | Adjust moisture levels. |
| Tough, dry crumb | Overdevelopment of gluten | Add hygroscopic agent (e.g., sorbitol or other sugar alcohol) to aid in moisture retention. Add starches or gums to bind water. |

| | | |
|---|---|---|
| Microbial spoilage and short shelf life | Water activity too high | Add agents such as glycerin or sorbitol that lower water activity.<br>Add preservative. |
| Coarse, irregular crumb | Improper creaming | Increase creaming time. |
| | Poor aeration | Use an alternative sweetener with larger granules.<br>Add emulsifier. |

## COOKIES

| Symptom | Causes | Changes to Make |
|---|---|---|
| Surface cracking when none desired | Sweetener preferentially absorbs water, causing separations in the dough matrix | Decrease sweetener level.<br>Add fructose or a hygroscopic sugar alcohol (e.g., sorbitol or xylitol). |
| No snap, texture too soft | Little or no recrystallization of sugar | Increase sucrose content.<br>Decrease level of hygroscopic agents (e.g., sugar alcohols).<br>Decrease liquids content.<br>Increase fat content.<br>Add polydextrose to increase hardness and fracturability. |
| Excessive surface cracking when some desired | Too much sucrose | Decrease sucrose level. |
| | Absence of reducing sugars | Increase hygroscopic agents (e.g., sugar alcohols or fructose). |
| Texture too hard (chewy desired) | Recrystallization of sugar throughout product | Decrease nutritive sweetener content. |
| | Low moisture content of final product | Add a hygroscopic agent (e.g., sugar alcohol or fructose).<br>Increase moisture level.<br>Decrease baking time. |
| Not enough spread | No or low nutritive sweetener melt | Increase nutritive sweetener content. |
| | Dough viscosity too high | Add a plasticizing agent (e.g., fat, sugar alcohol, or emulsifier).<br>Increase moisture content. |

## CHEMICALLY LEAVENED PRODUCTS

| Symptom | Causes | Changes to Make |
|---|---|---|
| Low volume of final product | Improper pH balance for leavening system | Adjust pH with sodium bicarbonate (especially if polydextrose was used). |
| | Poor aeration | Increase egg content. |
| Dry crumb, texture too airy | Low moisture level | Add a humectant (e.g., sugar alcohol).<br>Increase moisture content.<br>Decrease baking time.<br>Increase fat content. |

## FROZEN BAKERY PRODUCTS

| Symptom | Causes | Changes to Make |
|---|---|---|
| Poor freeze-thaw stability | Level of high molecular weight carbohydrates too low | Add or increase level of sugar alcohol, maltodextrins, or water-binding starches or gums. |
| Ice formation | Level of low molecular weight carbohydrates too low | Use a maltodextrin with higher dextrose equivalent. Increase level of simple sugars. |

## FROSTINGS AND ICINGS

| Symptom | Causes | Changes to Make |
|---|---|---|
| Gritty, sandy texture | Alternative sweetener granules too large | Use an alternative sweetener with smaller granules. |
| | Alternative sweetener not completely dissolved (boiled icings) | Increase boiling time. |
| Cracking, formation of a hard shell | Dehydration | Add hygroscopic agents (e.g., fructose or sugar alcohols). |
| | Moisture migration | Equalize water activity of product and frosting. |
| Poor adhesion | Excessive moisture | Decrease liquid levels in formulation. Add water-binding agents (e.g., starches or gums). Allow product to cool completely before finishing. |
| Icing sticks to wrapper or packaging | Level of hygroscopic agents too high | Increase sucrose level. Decrease level of hygroscopic agents (e.g., fructose or hygroscopic sugar alcohols). |
| | Product not completely cooled before finishing. | Allow product to cool completely. |
| Too soft | Excessive moisture | Decrease liquid levels. Add water-binding agents (e.g., starches or gums). |

## READY-TO-EAT CEREALS

| Symptom | Causes | Changes to Make |
|---|---|---|
| Clumping after coating | Insufficient drying | Increase drying time and/or temperature. Increase agitation during product coating and drying. |
| | Coating solution is too viscous (hygroscopic) | Decrease level of hygroscopic agents (e.g., fructose or sugar alcohols). |
| Cloudy coating appearance | Low solubility of alternative sweetener or solids replacer | Increase boiling time to ensure complete dissolution. Decrease solids content. Increase water content. |

| GRANOLA BARS | | |
|---|---|---|
| **Symptom** | **Causes** | **Changes to Make** |
| Too hard | Moisture content too low | Increase moisture content. Add hygroscopic agent (e.g., sugar alcohol or fructose). |
| | Too much bulking agent added | Decrease amount of bulking agent. |
| Too sticky, soft, or chewy | Hygroscopicity of final product too high | Decrease level of hygroscopic agents (e.g., fructose or sugar alcohols). |
| | Moisture content too high | Decrease moisture level. Increase baking time and/or temperature. |
| Crumbly texture | Poor binding (cohesiveness) | Increase moisture content. Add a hygroscopic agent (e.g., sugar alcohol or fructose). Decrease amount of bulking agent. Apply more coating. |

## References

1. Alexander, R. J. 1998. *Sweeteners: Nutritive.* American Association of Cereal Chemists, St. Paul, MN.
2. Freeman, T. M. 1989. Sweetening cakes and cake mixes with alitame. Cereal Foods World 34:1013-1015.
3. Peck, A. 1994. Use of acesulfame K in light and sugar-free baked goods. Cereal Foods World 39:743-745.
4. Barndt, R. L., and Jackson, G. 1990. Stability of sucralose in baked goods. Food Tech. 44:62-66.
5. Altschul, A. M. 1993. *Low-Calorie Foods Handbook.* Marcel Dekker, New York.
6. Khan, R. 1993. *Low Calorie Foods and Food Ingredients.* Blackie Academic and Professional, Glasgow, Scotland.
7. Ang, J. F., and Miller, W. B. 1991. Multiple functions of powdered cellulose as a food ingredient. Cereal Foods World 36:558-564.
8. Frye, A. M., and Setser C. S. 1992. Optimizing texture of reduced-calorie yellow layer cakes. Cereal Chem. 69:338-343.
9. Dartey, C. K., and Briggs, R. H. 1987. Reduced calorie baked goods and methods for producing same. U.S. patent 4,668,519.

# Other Applications

## Beverages

Low-calorie, or diet, beverages have become popular around the world, and alternative sweeteners have played a large role in their success. Formulations developed today provide clean, sweet flavors without bitter, metallic, or other off-flavors. High-intensity sweeteners are used extensively in these formulations. Although they can be used alone, they are often used in combination to mask off-flavors or to lower production costs. Sugar alcohols are not widely used in liquid beverage formulations as sweetening agents because they have a laxative effect at the levels needed to achieve sweetness. They can be used at low levels to provide mouthfeel and body, but starches, gums, and other hydrocolloids are used more widely.

### CARBONATED AND STILL BEVERAGES

Carbonated and still (noncarbonated) drinks containing alternative sweeteners are a large segment of the beverage industry. Low-calorie carbonated sodas, also called soft drinks or "pop," and non-carbonated beverages such as juices and sports drinks are widely available.

Traditional formulations of these drinks typically contain 10% sweetener, which provides mouthfeel and body as well as sweetness to the final product. They also often include acids, flavors, juices, and preservatives. Still beverage formulations may also contain gums and starches to help inhibit separation of ingredients such as low-density flavor oils. Alternatively sweetened carbonated and still beverage formulations do not differ significantly from their full-calorie counterparts. They generally consist of alternative sweeteners (at a level of 0.01–8%, depending on the product and sweetener used), acids, flavors, juices, preservatives, buffers, and, if necessary, bulking agents. Blends of traditional and alternative sweeteners or of different alternative sweeteners are also used. Bulking agents such as starches, natural or synthetic gums, and maltodextrins can be added to help provide the body and mouthfeel that may be lost when traditional sweeteners such as sucrose or high-fructose corn syrups are removed. Polydextrose used at levels of 3–5% in beverage formulations provides mouthfeel and rounds out flavors (1). Hydrogenated starch hydrolysates (HSHs) provide mouthfeel and inhibit microbial activity. The texture and mouthfeel of alternatively sweetened soft drink formulations can also be improved by increasing the carbon dioxide levels.

Several factors should be considered in choosing an alternative sweetener for a beverage formulation: quality of taste, ease of incorporation into the processing steps, stability at various levels of pH (about 2.5–8.0), heat stability (during pasteurization or ultra-high-temperature processing), and solubility. Usage levels of high-intensity sweeteners can range from 0.01 to 10%, depending on the desired characteristics of the final product and the sweetener chosen. As mentioned above, blends of alternative sweeteners are often used. The high-intensity sweeteners saccharin, acesulfame potassium (acesulfame K), stevioside, and cyclamates all benefit from synergistic blends (e.g., to enhance taste or stability or to mask off-flavors) (2), and including aspartame in some blends increases shelf life.

**Saccharin.** Although it is stable in soft drink applications, saccharin is rarely used alone in these formulations because of the bitter and metallic aftertastes that it can impart to the final product. Cyclamate effectively masks the aftertaste of saccharin, and blends of cyclamate and saccharin were popular in the United States until cyclamate was banned. These blends are still used in countries where cyclamate is approved for use. Sucrose, acesulfame K, and aspartame also mask saccharin's aftertastes. Blends of saccharin and aspartame are often used in the United States in fountain (food-service) applications. Formulations designed for this purpose are concentrated (3) and then later mixed with water and carbonated. They are generally more acidic than beverages prepared for retail sale, and aspartame degrades under these conditions (4). The saccharin in the blend helps to maintain sweetness and extend the shelf life of the product.

**Cyclamate.** Although cyclamates are banned in the United States, they are approved for use in several countries and are used in beverage applications. Cyclamate effectively masks the off-flavors of saccharin in these formulas but has a slow onset and can leave a lingering sweet or sour aftertaste.

**Acesulfame K.** Acesulfame K is stable in many drink applications, but because of its metallic aftertaste, it is not often used alone. Typically, it is blended with aspartame, which masks its off-flavor. It forms synergistic blends with aspartame and sucrose (Fig. 6-1), and its sweetening ability is greater at pH levels below neutral (5).

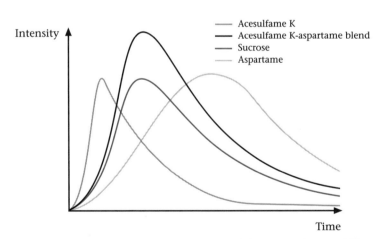

Fig. 6-1. Time-intensity profiles. (Adapted from Nutrinova, 1996, Beverages—In Duet with Sunett, Tech. Bull., Nutrinova, Somerset, NJ)

**Aspartame.** Aspartame is one of the most widely used alternative sweeteners in soft drink formulations in the United States. As discussed above, it is not stable at low pH (<3) and degrades in fountain formulas, which are highly acidic. Aspartame is used in these formulations to match the taste of the retail product but is blended with saccharin to provide stability. The shelf life of aspartame in beverage formulations is also affected by length of storage and temperature. Degradation occurs over time and is accelerated as temperature increases. Aspartame works well in fruit-flavored and citrus applications and enhances these flavors.

**Alitame.** Alitame is stable in many beverage applications. It is used in carbonated and still beverages in countries where it is approved for use. Off-flavors in certain products have been noted after storage (5).

**Sucralose.** Sucralose is very stable in beverage applications and provides a very clean, sweet taste, although in some formulations, the taste can linger (2). Sucralose can be used in beverages that are preserved with heat (e.g., light juice drinks).

**Thaumatin.** Thaumatin is a natural high-intensity sweetener with a licorice-type flavor that enhances coffee flavors and can also be used to mask the bitter notes of saccharin. Its sweetening effect can be significantly reduced in formulas that contain high concentrations of gums such as locust bean, xanthan, carrageenan, alginate, or carboxymethyl cellulose (6), and it may also precipitate with these ingredients (5). Thaumatin can also react with colors, but the addition of gum arabic reduces this effect (5).

## ALCOHOLIC BEVERAGES

In alcoholic beverages, traditional sweeteners provide a nutrient source for yeasts, resulting in fermentation and the production of alcohol. They either occur naturally (e.g., through malting processes) or are added to the formulation to aid fermentation. Nutritive sweeteners are thus an essential part of the production of alcoholic beverages, and since alternative sweeteners cannot be used by yeasts, they are unable to perform the same necessary function.

Traditional sweeteners also provide sweetness, body, and mouthfeel in products such as liqueurs and cordials, and alternative sweeteners can be used in these applications to produce reduced-calorie versions. It is important that the alternative sweetener be soluble in ethanol and that it not interfere with the delicate flavor balance of these products. Sucralose is one of the few alternative sweeteners that can be used in these applications (4). It withstands a wide range of pH and does not precipitate in the presence of ethanol. Sugar alcohols can also be used to sweeten these products. They provide mouthfeel and bulk, and those with a cooling effect, such as xylitol and sorbitol, can be beneficial in mint-flavored formulations.

## POWDERED DRINK MIXES

Sucrose is often used in traditionally sweetened powdered drink mixes and provides sweetness, bulk, viscosity, and mouthfeel. Alternatively sweetened mixes, such as sugar-free or reduced-calorie cocoas, fruit punches, lemonades, fruit-flavored mixes, and flavored coffees, are also widely available. The factors that should be considered in the choice of an alternative sweetener for use in these formulations are the same as those discussed in the carbonated and still beverage section. Both high-intensity sweeteners and sugar alcohols can be used in dry mix beverage applications, and their features are also reviewed above.

Product developers do face some unique challenges in formulating these mixes with alternative sweeteners. One is the problem of portion control. If a high-intensity sweetener is used, so little is needed to replace the nutritive sweetener that the bulk of the final product is reduced and it may be difficult for the consumer to make a single serving. Thus, it may be necessary to add soluble fillers such as maltodextrins or polydextrose to increase bulk. Second, if hygroscopic sugar alcohols are used, proper packaging must to used to inhibit them from caking during long-term storage.

# Dairy Products

Sweetened dairy products include ice creams, frozen yogurts and other types of frozen desserts, yogurts, and milk-based puddings. Nutritive sweeteners provide the desired sweetness and fill various other roles. For example, in yogurts and puddings, they provide body and texture. In frozen dairy products, they provide body and texture and also lower the freezing point. Reduced-calorie and no-sugar-added versions of these products have been formulated with both high-intensity sweeteners and sugar alcohols. The goal of product developers is to maintain the characteristics of the original products, especially the sweetness level, while lowering the sugar content.

## ICE CREAM AND FROZEN DESSERTS

Although the formulations and processing steps vary depending on the final product desired (e.g., ice cream versus sherbets or ices), the basic principles of using high-intensity sweeteners and sugar alcohols in reduced-sugar (i.e., "light") or no-sugar-added frozen products are generally the same. As mentioned above, the ability to lower the freezing point of a product is an important attribute of nutritive sweeteners. In general, frozen products containing nutritive sweeteners are less solid at a given temperature than the same products without sweeteners. This characteristic is significant because it allows the product to melt down smoothly on the tongue, keeps the product from becoming so hard that it cannot be easily scooped and served when removed from the freezer, and makes the formation of ice crystals in the product less likely. Because their usage levels are so low (typically 0.05–0.5%), high-intensity sweeteners cannot lower the freezing point of these products. The sugar alcohols sorbitol, lactitol, xylitol, and isomalt can be used to achieve this effect and are often used in frozen desserts and ice creams (7). Maltitol, mannitol, and HSHs can also be used. Sorbitol lowers the freezing point and inhibits the crystallization of other sugars (such as lactose) present in the mix. The ability of lactitol to lower the freezing point is similar to that of sucrose, and the hygroscopicity and solubility of the two are also similar. Unlike lactose, lactitol does not cause a sandy texture in ice cream and frozen dessert products. Xylitol can also lower the freezing point, but if it is used as the sole sweetener, the melting properties of the product are poor and it becomes too soft (8), requiring the addition of thickening agents such as gums. Isomalt also lowers the freezing point but can crystallize because of its low solubility when used at levels greater than 15% (7). HSHs have a slight effect on lowering the freezing point and are helpful in improving the *freeze-thaw stability* of a product.

Many high-intensity sweeteners can be used in frozen dairy applications. Although frozen storage helps to extend the shelf life of these sweeteners, the pH levels of products can vary and the stability of a particular sweetener under these conditions should be considered. The best time during the production process to add the sweetener should also be considered. Sweeteners that are less heat stable can be added with the flavoring. Sugar alcohols or polydextrose can be added to lower the freezing point, and polydextrose also helps to create a creamy texture. Another problem is the loss of bulk solids. Increasing the milk solids nonfat (MSNF) of the mix is one solution, although it may be necessary to hydrolyze the lactose in the MSNF so that it does not cause a sandy texture in the final product. Gums soluble in cold water, such as carrageenan, guar, locust bean, carboxymethyl cellulose, and microcrystalline cellulose, can also be used to increase bulk. In addition, they improve texture, control crystallization, and enhance meltdown of the final product.

## YOGURT AND PUDDING-TYPE PRODUCTS

Lactose is a naturally occurring milk sugar used by microorganisms during fermentation in the production of yogurt. The acid produced during fermentation is responsible for the gelling and setting of yogurt's unique texture, which can vary from thin to thick and custard-like. It is not often necessary to add other nutritive sweeteners to aid the fermentation process, but they are added to yogurts and pudding-type products to provide sweetness, body, texture, and mouthfeel. In reduced-sugar or no-sugar-added products, high-intensity sweeteners are used for sweetening. The pH of yogurt systems is typically about 4–4.5, and most high-intensity sweeteners can be used at this level. Aspartame is widely used in yogurt formulations because it is most stable at this pH level and because it enhances the fruit flavors of

**Freeze-thaw stability**—Ability of a product to withstand cold temperature cycling and/or prolonged storage at reduced temperatures.

these products. Starches, polydextrose, or gums are used to replace bulk solids, provide body and mouthfeel, and maintain creaminess.

# Preserved Fruits and Vegetables

Fruits and vegetables can be preserved in a variety of ways, including drying, freezing, and canning. Fruits can also be preserved as jams, jellies, and preserves. The various roles that nutritive sweeteners play in these products are reviewed elsewhere (9).

One important characteristic of nutritive sweeteners in these applications is that they increase the osmotic pressure of solutions. During freezing and canning, fruits are often submerged in syrups containing nutritive sweeteners. The increased osmotic pressure causes water from the tissues of the fruits or vegetables to diffuse into the syrup solution. As a result, cell damage decreases and cell preservation occurs. Syrups used during freezing processes also help to decrease diffusion of oxygen into the tissues, reducing browning and lipid oxidation, which can cause the tissues to soften. In dehydrated fruits and vegetables and products such as jams, nutritive sweeteners lower the water activity, which inhibits microbial growth.

When alternative sweeteners are used, product attributes and formulations may be altered. The bulk lost upon removal of the sugars may need to be replaced, and ingredient functionalities may change, depending upon the effects of the other ingredients in the formula.

## JAMS, JELLIES, AND PRESERVES

The basic formulation of a jam, jelly, or preserve containing traditional sweeteners usually includes fruit (fruit pieces, fruit juice, or whole fruit, depending upon the product), sugar, pectin, and acid. The solids range from 65 to 70% and are mostly in the form of soluble solids present as naturally occurring fruit sugars and added sucrose. Pectin is added to ensure gel formation and can be either high methoxy pectin or low methoxy pectin. High methoxy pectin requires sugar and acid (pH 2.9–3.6). Low methoxy pectin does not require acidic conditions. It depends instead upon the presence of calcium, which forms "bridges" between pectin molecules, resulting in gel formation.

In formulating reduced-sugar or no-sugar-added products, the developer must compensate for the changes in sweetness, bulk, texture, and gelling properties. Many of the high-intensity sweeteners can be used to achieve sweetness. Those that are not heat stable can be added toward the end of the process after heating and before gelation. The sweetener must be stable at low pH levels. Aspartame is commonly used because of its ability to enhance fruit flavors and its stability at various pH levels. Other high-intensity sweeteners such as sucralose, acesulfame K, and alitame also provide clean, sweet flavors in these products. Sugar alcohols can be used to provide both sweetness and bulk. Sorbitol, lactitol, HSHs, and maltitol can be used with good results (1), and they also inhibit the crystallization of any sucrose present in the formula. Xylitol can also be used but can crystallize if it represents >40% of the solids in the formula. Isomalt can also crystallize if present at >25%. Other ingredients that can be used to provide bulk include gums such as carrageenan and locust bean gum. Since high methoxy pectin requires sugars for gel formation, it may be necessary to use low methoxy pectin and add calcium to low-sugar formulations.

## CANNED FOODS

In producing no-sugar-added or low-sugar canned foods, the possible changes in sweetness, bulk, and texture should be considered. Sweetness can be achieved with high-intensity sweeteners or sugar alcohols. Using sugar alcohols alone or in combination with gums can also help to provide bulk and viscosity. A reverse of the osmotic pressure described above may occur with the use of high-intensity sweeteners and bulking agents, especially in canned fruits. Because the concentration of sugars is higher in the fruit tissue than in the surrounding solution, the water in the solution diffuses into the fruit, causing an increase in osmotic pressure in the tissue and a final product with a firm texture, which can be a desirable attribute.

# Meats and Seafoods

Alternative sweeteners can be used successfully in meat and seafood products to achieve the desired product attributes. In cured meats such as ham and bacon, the sweet flavors can be achieved with heat-stable high-intensity sweeteners. These sweeteners provide an advantage over nutritive sweeteners in the final products because they do not participate in Maillard browning or caramelization reactions. Thus, they remain stable during consumer preparation steps such as frying and do not contribute to charring or burning. Sugar alcohols (e.g., sorbitol) are used in the production of manufactured seafood products such as *surimi*. They act as cryoprotectants and prevent denaturation of the fish proteins.

**Surimi**—Japanese word referring to imitation seafood (e.g., crab or lobster) produced by mincing and reforming fish meat along with added flavors.

# Troubleshooting

| JAMS, JELLIES, AND PRESERVES | | |
|---|---|---|
| Symptom | Causes | Changes to Make |
| Gritty or sandy texture | Crystallization of sugar alcohol or nutritive sweetener | Decrease level of crystallizable sugar alcohols (e.g., xylitol or isomalt). Increase or add sorbitol. |
| Spoilage | Water activity too high | Increase sorbitol content. Add preservative. |

| Thin consistency or lack of structure | Gel strength too low | If high methoxy pectin was used, change to low methoxy pectin.<br>If low methoxy pectin was used, check pH and/or add more pectin or calcium, if necessary. |
|---|---|---|
| Texture too hard or structure brittle | Gel strength too high | If low methoxy pectin was used, check pH and/or decrease pectin or calcium levels, if necessary. |
| Low sweetness level | Degradation of alternative sweetener | Check stability of alternative sweetener under processing, storage, and pH conditions. |
| Not enough body | Low solids level | Add gums (e.g., locust bean gum or carrageenan). |

## BEVERAGES, LIQUID

| Symptom | Causes | Changes to Make |
|---|---|---|
| Lacks body and/or mouthfeel | Low viscosity or solids content | Add sugar alcohols, starches, pectins, gums, and/or maltodextrins. |
| Off-flavor or odor | Microbial or yeast growth | Check quality of incoming ingredients. |
| Low sweetness level | Degradation of alternative sweetener | Check stability of alternative sweetener under processing, storage, and pH conditions. |

## BEVERAGES, POWDERED MIXES

| Symptom | Causes | Changes to Make |
|---|---|---|
| Caking | Improper granulation of bulking agent and/or alternative sweetener | Increase size of granules.<br>Use anticaking agents.<br>Store ingredients in dry environment. |
| Not homogeneous | Settling of large particles | Decrease size of granules of ingredients. |
| Poor dispersion into solution | Poor particle wettabililty | Increase size of granules.<br>Agglomerate product. |

## BEVERAGES, ALCOHOLIC

| Symptom | Causes | Changes to Make |
|---|---|---|
| Off colors (e.g., in white liqueurs or cordials) | Excessive Maillard browning | Decrease level of reducing sugars.<br>Increase level of sugar alcohol or high-intensity sweetener. |
| Sedimentation | Precipitation of alternative sweetener | Choose an alternative sweetener that does not precipitate in the presence of alcohol. |

## YOGURTS AND PUDDINGS

| Symptom | Causes | Changes to Make |
|---|---|---|
| Low sweetness level | Degradation of alternative sweetener | Check stability of alternative sweetener under processing, storage, and pH conditions. |
| Lacks body or texture | Low solids content | Add starches and/or gums. |

| FROZEN DESSERTS | | |
|---|---|---|
| **Symptom** | **Causes** | **Changes to Make** |
| Too hard | Freezing point too high | Increase sugar alcohol or high-intensity sweetener level. |
| Too soft; icy; weak body | Freezing point too low | Add sugar alcohol (e.g., hydrogenated starch hydrolysate). |
| | Low solids content | Increase milk solids nonfat (MSNF) level. |
| Chewy or gummy texture | Excessive moisture binding by ingredients | Decrease sugar alcohol level. Adjust stabilizer level. |
| Sandy or gritty texture | Excessive lactose crystallization | Decrease lactose content (especially if MSNF level was increased). Add a crystal inhibitor (e.g., sorbitol). |

## References

1. Altschul, A. M. 1993. *Low-Calorie Foods Handbook*. Marcel Dekker, New York.
2. Curtis, L. 1998. Pop art: Designing soft drinks. Prep. Foods, Jan., pp. 41-67.
3. Holleran, J. 1996. Sweet success: Use of high intensity sweeteners in soft drinks. Beverage Ind. 87(4):50-52.
4. Mancini, S. 1994. Less filling, more stable. Beverage World 113:62-64.
5. Grenby, T. H. 1989. *Progress in Sweeteners*. Applied Food Science Series. Elsevier, New York.
6. Anonymous. 1996. Thaumatin—The sweetest substance known to man has a wide range of food applications. Food Technol. 50:74-75.
7. Khan, R. 1993. *Low Calorie Foods and Food Ingredients*. Chapman and Hall, New York.
8. Hyvonen, L., Koivistoinen, P., and Voirol, F. 1982. Food technicological evaluation of xylitol. Adv. Food Res. 28:373-403.
9. Alexander, R. J. 1998. *Sweeteners: Nutritive*. American Association of Cereal Chemists, St. Paul, MN.

# Special Topics

## Product Development

Foods containing alternative sweeteners are developed and marketed to meet the needs of specific consumer groups, e.g., those who wish to lower their caloric intake by decreasing the amount of sugars they consume and those who wish to lower their risk of dental caries. Diabetics are also concerned about sugar levels in foods. While a final product may meet the needs of all of these consumers, it is important that the product developer understand the factors behind each of these consumer needs.

### REDUCED-SUGAR AND REDUCED-CALORIE FOODS

Recent medical research has shown a correlation between diet and many health-related issues such as cardiovascular disease, high blood pressure, cancer, high cholesterol levels, and obesity (1–4). During the 1990s, there was an increase in the number of reduced-calorie products in the marketplace in direct response to consumer interest in weight loss. Calorie reduction was achieved in many of these foods by reformulating traditional products to include less sugar and/or fat (reduced-fat foods are reviewed elsewhere [1,3,5]). However, reducing either or both of these ingredients creates an imbalance in the formula. Depending on the product, low-calorie ingredients such as fibers, polydextrose (1 calories per gram), or water (0 calories per gram) can be used to correct these imbalances (see Chapters 4–6 for details concerning the formulation of specific products).

How does the alternatively sweetened product help the consumer lose weight? Traditional sweeteners, which contain 4 calories per gram of food substance, are replaced with high-intensity sweeteners or sugar alcohols, and low-calorie bulking agents are added to solve any functionality problems or correct formula imbalance. Lowering the fat and sugar content lowers the total caloric value of the food because these substances are replaced with ingredients with fewer calories.

High-intensity sweeteners provide the same amount of sweetness as traditional sweeteners at significantly lower usage levels, and since most pass through the digestive system unchanged, they do not contribute to the caloric value of the food. The caloric values of the high-intensity sweeteners reviewed in this text are shown in Table 7-1. Aspartame and thaumatin have caloric values of 4 calories per gram because they contain peptide bonds, which provide energy during

**TABLE 7-1.** Caloric Values of High-Intensity Sweeteners

| Sweetener | Calories per gram |
|---|---|
| Aspartame | 4 |
| Alitame | 1.4[a] |
| Thaumatin | 4 |
| Saccharin | 0 |
| Cyclamate | 0 |
| Acesulfame K | 0 |
| Glycyrrhizin | 0 |
| Stevioside | 0 |
| Sucralose | 0 |

[a] Petition filed with FDA.

**TABLE 7-2.** Caloric Values of Sugar Alcohols in the United States

| Sugar Alcohol | Calories per gram |
|---|---|
| Sorbitol | 2.6 |
| Mannitol | 1.6 |
| Xylitol | 2.4 |
| Lactitol | 2.0 |
| Maltitol | 2.1 |
| Isomalt[a] | 2.0 |
| HSHs[b] | 3.0 |

[a] Palatinit.
[b] Hydrogenated starch hydrolysates.

digestion. However, because they can be used in such small amounts, their contribution to the total caloric content is negligible.

Sugar alcohols both sweeten and provide bulk to reformulated products. They can be used alone or in combination with high-intensity sweeteners and other bulking agents. The caloric values of the sugar alcohols reviewed in this text are shown in Table 7-2. When formulating a reduced-calorie food with sugar alcohols, the developer must check the final caloric value, because the total savings in calories may not be significant enough to meet a product claim.

Do reduced-calorie foods have an impact on the prevalence of obesity? It is estimated that 60% of the calories in a typical American diet comes from fats and sugars and that 20% of the calories is from sugars alone (1). While high-fat foods obviously play a major role in the weight of individuals, foods containing high levels of sugars, such as cakes, cookies, and confections, also have a significant effect, and studies have shown that dieters are unwilling to give up these foods entirely. While the consumer may choose alternatively sweetened foods to help reduce caloric intake, portion control is essential in successfully lowering the overall daily caloric intake, thus allowing weight loss to occur (1,3).

## DENTAL CARIES

Dental caries, or tooth decay, are essentially areas of demineralization of the calcified tissues of the teeth caused by the bacterium *Streptococcus mutans*. Many factors are associated with the decay, including the microbial environment of the mouth, the structure of the teeth, and oral hygiene. A strong link between diet and dental caries has also been shown. An acidic environment (pH <5.5) within the mouth is necessary for decay to occur (4), and such an environment results from the fermentation of carbohydrates. The relationship between ingested sugar as a source of fermentable carbohydrate and the occurrence of dental caries is well documented (4).

The development of dental caries can be inhibited by several means. One is fluoride treatments. Another is to maintain a pH level greater than 5.5 in the mouth, which can be achieved by practicing oral hygiene and by removing sources of fermentable carbohydrates from the diet. Oral hygiene removes sources of fermentable carbohydrates after eating and keeps pH levels within the desirable range. Some sources of fermentable carbohydrates can be removed from the diet by using sugar-free products such as chewing gums, soft drinks, and confections instead of the traditional products. Neither high-intensity sweeteners nor sugar alcohols can be fermented by *S. mutans*. In vitro studies of *S. mutans* showed lower growth rates in mannitol and sorbitol than in glucose (4). Other studies have shown that its growth is also inhibited by xylitol and hydrogenated starch hydrolysates (HSHs). Many studies have shown that xylitol is beneficial in inhibiting the growth of *S. mutans* and that it is one of the most effective sugar substitutes in chewing gums for preventing dental caries (6–9).

## DIABETES

Diabetes mellitus is a metabolic disorder that affects many people around the world. In people with normal metabolism, most of the carbohydrate consumed is broken down into the simple sugar glucose, which is transported in the blood and used by cells for energy and growth. The body needs insulin, a hormone secreted by the pancreas, to regulate blood glucose levels. In individuals with diabetes, little or no insulin is produced or that which is produced does not function properly. As a result, blood glucose levels rise after a meal and remain high. High levels of glucose can be detected in the urine, and the cells do not receive what they need to function properly. If left unmanaged, diabetes can lead to health complications such as blindness, kidney failure, heart disease, stroke, and even death. There are three types of diabetes. Individuals with type I diabetes produce no insulin and require daily injections of the hormone. Those with type II diabetes produce insulin, but it is either insufficient or inactive. The third type, gestational diabetes, occurs in some pregnant women. The condition usually disappears after the pregnancy but may recur later in a woman's life.

The management of diabetes includes several factors, including diet, which has a direct effect on the blood glucose levels of all three types of diabetics. It used to be assumed that limiting sugar intake was important in regulating blood glucose levels, and many people with diabetes were instructed to avoid foods such as cakes, cookies, and confections. While it is true that sugary foods raise blood glucose levels, more recent research has shown that all carbohydrates ingested have this effect. In 1994, the American Diabetes Association's nutrition principles were changed to reflect this research. They now state that monitoring the total carbohydrate intake, not the types of carbohydrates eaten, is crucial for blood sugar control.

However, when monitoring total carbohydrate intake, a person with diabetes must still consider the amount consumed in high-sugar foods. Numerous products containing alternative sweeteners have been developed that do not cause a significant increase in blood sugar levels. Because high-intensity sweeteners do not metabolize to glucose and are present at very low levels in foods, they do not cause a rise in blood glucose levels. Sugar alcohols can also be used in formulating these foods. Sorbitol, maltitol, and HSHs are partially metabolized into glucose but at such low levels that they do not significantly affect blood glucose levels. Xylitol, lactitol, mannitol, and isomalt are independent of insulin regulation and also do not significantly raise blood glucose levels.

# Nutrition Labeling and Nutrient Content Claims

Regulations concerning nutrition labeling and nutrient content claims in the United States were established by the 1990 Nutrition Labeling and Education Act (NLEA) and are enforced by the Food and Drug Administration (FDA). They can be found in the *U.S. Code of Federal Regulations* under Title 21.

## NUTRITION LABELING

Declaration on the nutrition label is mandatory for some nutrients and voluntary for others. "Sugars" are defined as the sum of all mono- and disaccharides present in the food product (whether added or occurring naturally), and the labeling of sugars is mandatory. "Sugar alcohols" are defined as the sum of all saccharide derivatives in which the hydroxyl group replaces a ketone or aldehyde group and whose use in food is listed by the FDA or is classified as Generally Recognized as Safe. Labeling sugar alcohols on the nutrition panel is voluntary. However, if a sugar or sugar alcohol content claim is made or if sugar alcohols are added as ingredients (as opposed to those that are naturally present), the labeling becomes mandatory. Those added as ingredients must also be listed in the ingredient statement. Labeling of high-intensity sweeteners is not required on the nutrition label, but, like all food ingredients, they must be included in the ingredient statement if they are added as components of the food.

## NUTRIENT CONTENT CLAIMS

The NLEA also defined several nutrient content claims for foods. The definitions for nutrient content claims involving sugar are as follows:

> *Sugar free*—must contain less than 0.5 g of sugars per reference amount of the food. The term cannot apply to an ingredient that is a sugar or is generally understood to contain sugars. Products must also be labeled with a "low calorie" or "reduced calorie" claim. If the product is not low or reduced calorie, a qualifying statement such as "not for weight control" must be made.
> *Low sugar*—not defined. No recommended intake given.
> *Reduced* or *less sugar*—must contain at least 25% less sugar per reference amount than the appropriate reference food.
> *No added sugars* (or *Without added sugars*)—claim may be made only if no sugar or sugar-containing ingredients are added during processing.

The definitions for calorie-reduced foods are as follows:

*Reduced calorie*—must contain a minimum of 25% fewer calories per reference amount than the appropriate reference food.

*Low calorie*—must contain less than 40 calories per reference amount or per 50 g if the reference amount is small.

*Light*—If 50% or more of the calories are from fat, fat must be reduced by 50% per reference amount. If less than 50% of the calories are from fat, fat must be reduced by at least one-half *or* calories by at least one-third per reference amount.

*Diet*—applies to soft drinks. If "diet" was in the brand name prior to October 25, 1989, the product is exempt from the nutrient content claim regulations.

## OTHER LABEL INFORMATION

The use of certain alternative sweeteners in products in the United States may require additional labeling information.

**Information for phenylketonuriacs.** Persons born with a condition called phenylketonuria must monitor their dietary intake of phenylalanine. Because these individuals cannot metabolize this amino acid, brain damage can result. Since phenylalanine is a component and metabolite of aspartame, products that contain this sweetener must be labeled with the warning, "Phenylketonuriacs: contains phenylalanine."

**Saccharin content warning.** Saccharin has long been a subject of controversy in the United States (see Chapter 1). Currently, the FDA requires that products containing saccharin carry the following statement on the container: "Use of this product may be hazardous to your health. This product contains saccharin which has been determined to cause cancer in laboratory animals."

**Laxative effect warning.** Bulking agents such as sugar alcohols and polydextrose can cause laxation if ingested in large amounts (see Bulking Agents below). Warning labels are required on products containing these ingredients.

# Bulking Agents

## GASTROINTESTINAL PROBLEMS

Several components used as bulking agents in foods, including fibers, polydextrose, and sugar alcohols, can cause mild flatulence or laxation when ingested. These side effects are caused by the slow degradation process and the increased osmotic pressure that these components can create in the gastrointestinal tract. These bulking agents are often used in alternatively sweetened foods and can be a concern in the consumption of these foods. In general, the effects of disaccharide sugar alcohols such as isomalt, lactitol, and maltitol (as well as HSHs) are less than those of monosaccharide sugar alcohols such as sorbitol and xylitol. Flatulence and laxation also depend upon the amount of the causative agent eaten, other foods consumed at the same time, and the individual's tolerance. In the United States, if 50 g of sorbitol, 20 g of mannitol, or 15 g of polydextrose is likely to be consumed per day, a statement warning about the possible laxative effect is required. It has been noted that those who consume these components on a regular basis can adapt to them and that there is an eventual decrease in the flatulence and/or laxative effect.

**TABLE 7-3.** Low-Calorie Carbohydrate Bulking Agents[a]

| Polysaccharide | Composition | Properties | Source | Food Applications |
|---|---|---|---|---|
| Pectin | poly($\alpha$-D-Galacto-pyranosyluronic acid) with various contents of methyl ester groups | Gelling, thickening | Fruits, vegetables | Jams, jellies, low-sugar or sugar-free jams and jellies, beverages, milk products |
| D-Glucan | $\beta$-(1→4)-D-Glucose, $\beta$-(1→3)-D-glucose | Bulking | Cereals (barley, oats) | Breakfast cereals |
| Galactomannan (guar gum, locust bean gum) | $\beta$-(1→4)-D-Manno-pyranosyl (backbone) and $\alpha$-(1→6)-D-galac-topyranosyl | Thickening, stabilizing | *Cyamopsis tetra-gonolobus* (guar gum), *Ceratonia siliqua* (locust bean gum) | Sauces, salad dressings, ice cream, frozen foods |
| Carrageenan | Mixture of sulfated polysaccharides containing $\alpha$-D-galactose and 3,6-anhydro-D-galactose | Thickening, gelling, protein reactivity | Rhodophyceae (red and blue algae) | Dairy products, bakery products, water gels, dessert gels, meat products, low-sugar jams and jellies |
| Agarose | $\beta$-D-Galactose and 3,6-anhydro-$\beta$-L-galactose linked-(1→3) | Gelling, stabilizing, emulsifying | Rhodophyceae | Dairy products, confections, bakery products, meat substitutes, desserts |
| Alginate | $\beta$-D-Mannopyranosyl-uronic acid and $\alpha$-L-gulopyranosyluronic acid | Water holding, gelling, emulsion stabilizing, thickening | Phaeophyceae (brown algae) | Dairy products, bakery products, dietetic products, salad dressings, dessert puddings and gels, beer foam, fabricated foods |
| Xanthan gum | $\beta$-(1→4)-D-Glucopyr-anosyl (backbone) and $\beta$-D-mannopyrano-syl-(1→4)-$\beta$-D-glucuronopyranosyl-(1→2)-6-O-acetyl-$\beta$-D-mannopyranosyl trisaccharide | Thickening | *Xanthomonas campestris* | Beverages, canned foods, frozen foods, salad dressings, gels and puddings |
| Cellulose | $\beta$-(1→4)-D-Gluco-pyranosyl | . . . | Many plants | . . . |
| Polydextrose | D-Glucose | Thickening, humectant | Synthetic | Low-calorie soft drinks and foods |

[a] Adapted from (3).

## FORMS OF BULKING AGENTS

In the development of alternatively sweetened foods, the product developer is faced with the task of either reformulating a food that contains traditional sweeteners or formulating a new food with high-intensity sweeteners to create a sweet-tasting final product. In both situations, the issue of what will make up the bulk of the food may need to be addressed. Other issues, such as body, texture, mouthfeel, air incorporation, freezing point depression, gelatinization, and crystallization, may also arise. Bulking agents can be used to help the developer solve these problems. Often, however, one bulking agent may not provide the entire solution, and a combination of agents may be needed.

Bulking agents are available in many different forms, e.g., sugar alcohols and polysaccharides (including gums and starches). The choice for a particular formulation depends on the attributes desired in the final product. The properties and uses of sugar alcohols have been discussed throughout this text. Starches provide bulk as well as calories. A review of starches and their applications in foods are reviewed elsewhere (10). An overview of low-calorie, polysaccharide-based bulking agents is given in Table 7-3.

Polydextrose, a nonsweet bulking agent commonly used in the development of alternatively sweetened foods, is a polymer of glucose, sorbitol, and citric acid (89:10:1). It is slightly acidic and very water soluble. Because its acidity can cause problems such as sucrose inversion and lipid rancidity in some foods, manufacturers have also developed neutralized forms of polydextrose. It is available in either liquid or powder form, and depending on the application need, the supplier can provide the form and acidity level necessary for a given formulation. Polydextrose works well in low- or reduced-calorie foods because it has only 1 calorie per gram. Its viscosity decreases with increasing temperatures and is greater than that of sorbitol. The viscosities of 70% solutions of polydextrose, sucrose, and sorbitol at various temperatures are shown in Figure 7-1. Because it acts as a humectant and cryoprotectant, polydextrose can help to extend shelf life. Applications with polydextrose that are reviewed in this text include baked goods, confections, fillings, and ice creams.

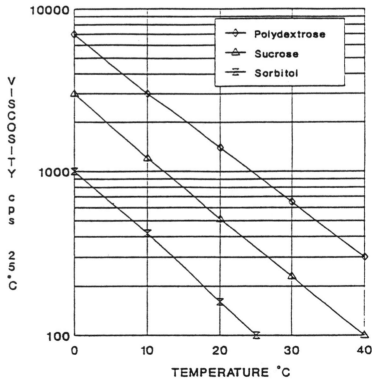

**Fig. 7-1.** Viscosity profiles of 70% solutions of polydextrose, sucrose, and sorbitol at various temperatures. (Reprinted, with permission, from F. K. Moppett, Polydextrose, pages 401-421 in: [11])

## References

1. Altschul, A. M. 1993. *Low-Calorie Foods Handbook.* Marcel Dekker, New York.
2. Alexander, R. J. 1998. *Sweeteners: Nutritive.* American Association of Cereal Chemists, St. Paul, MN.
3. Khan, R. 1993. *Low-Calorie Foods and Food Ingredients.* Blackie Academic and Professional, Glasgow, Scotland.
4. Rugg-Gunn, A. J. 1991. *Sugarless, The Way Forward.* Elsevier Applied Science, New York.
5. Stauffer, C. 1997. *Fats and Oils.* American Association of Cereal Chemists, St. Paul, MN.
6. Pepper, T., and Olinger, P. 1988. Xylitol in sugar-free confections. Food Technol. 42(10):98-106.
7. Uhari, M., Kontiokari, T., Koskela, M., and Niemela, M. 1996. Xylitol chewing gum in prevention of acute otitis media: Double blind randomized trial. Br. Med. J. 313:1180-1184.
8. Edgar, W. M. 1998. Sugar substitutes, chewing gum, and dental caries—A review. Br. Dent. J. 184:29-32.
9. Makinen, K. K. , Bennett, C. A., Hujoel, P. P., Isotupa, K. P., Pape H. R., Jr., and Makinen, P. L. 1995. Xylitol chewing gums and caries rates: A 40-month cohort study. J. Dent. Res. 74:1904-1913.
10. Thomas, D. J., and Atwell, W. A. 1999. *Starches.* American Association of Cereal Chemists, St. Paul, MN.
11. O'Brien Nabors, L., and Gelardi, R. C., Eds. 1991. *Alternative Sweeteners,* 2nd ed. Marcel Dekker, New York.

# Glossary

**Amphoteric**—Pertaining to a compound that has both positive and negative charges.

**Bulk sweetener**—Sweetener that also adds bulk.

**Caramelization**—A series of reactions that sucrose undergoes when heated, resulting in final reaction products such as brown pigments and caramel flavors.

**Cariogenic**—Capable of causing tooth decay (caries).

**Case hardening**—The formation of a hardened outer shell or skin over a softer or more liquid entity.

**Chelate**—To combine with to form a ring.

**Cold flow**—Loss of shape or structure of a candy piece during storage over time.

**Conching**—Slow mixing of a heated chocolate paste to reduce particle size and increase thickness and smoothness.

**Creaming**—The incorporation of air by rapidly mixing a crystalline substance into a solid substance (e.g., sugar into butter).

**Cyclize**—To form a ring structure in a chemical compound.

**Degrees Brix (°Brix)**—Measure of the density or concentration of a sugar solution. The degrees Brix equal the weight percent of sucrose in the solution.

**Delaney Clause**—A clause in the 1958 Food Additives Amendment forbidding the use of a substance in food if, after appropriate tests, any part of it was shown to cause cancer in humans or animals.

**Denaturation**—The process that proteins undergo when subjected to certain chemical or physical treatments (e.g., heating) that cause disruption of the noncovalent bonds that maintain their secondary and tertiary structure, resulting in profound changes in functional properties.

**Dextrose**—A six-carbon sugar; also called glucose.

**Dextrose equivalent (DE)**—A measure of the percentage of glucosidic bonds hydrolyzed; i.e., an indication of the reducing sugar content calculated as the percent anhydrous dextrose of the total dry substance. Pure dextrose has a DE of 100.

**Dihydrate**—A compound that contains two molecules of water.

**Dipeptide**—A combination of two peptides. A peptide is an amide resulting from the condensation of amino acids.

**Disaccharide**—A carbohydrate containing two sugar units, each composed of five or six carbon atoms in a furanose or pyranose ring.

**Diterpenoid**—A terpene with two isoprene units in its structure.

**Dry graining**—Development of a sandy texture caused by recrystallization of an ingredient.

**Endotherm**—A peak or curve that indicates the amount of energy resulting from a transition from one state to another.

**Fondant**—Grained confection often used as an ingredient in the manufacture of other candies such as fudge.

**Freeze-thaw stability**—Ability of a product to withstand cold temperature cycling and/or prolonged storage at reduced temperatures.

**Fructose**—A six-carbon keto sugar naturally present in fruits and honey and produced by the isomerization of glucose.

**Gelatinization**—Collapse (disruption) of molecular orders within starch granules manifested by irreversible changes in properties such as granular swelling, native crystalline melting, loss of birefringence, and starch solubilization.

**Glass**—Containing no crystallinity.

**Glucose**—A six-carbon simple sugar.

**Gluten**—The resultant product of mixing the wheat proteins gliadin and glutenin in the presence of water.

**GMPs**—Good Manufacturing Practices. The food-handling practices in the United States. They include general limits on the amounts of food additives used so that the total amount is only that which will achieve the desired effect in the food system.

**GRAS**—Generally Recognized as Safe. Pertains to food additives that experts have declared safe for use in foods on the basis of their history of use.

**Gum**—Water-soluble or modified polysaccharide used for thickening and water binding.

**Heat capacity**—The amount of heat needed to raise the temperature of a substance 1°C.

**Hexose**—A six-carbon simple sugar molecule (e.g., glucose).

**Hydrocolloid**—Gum; water-soluble or modified polysaccharide used for thickening and water binding.

**Hygroscopicity**—Ability to attract and retain moisture.

**Inversion**—The process by which sucrose hydrolyzes to its component sugars, fructose and glucose.

**Isoelectric point**—The pH level at which the number of positive charges is equal to the number of negative charges.

**Ketose**—A sugar molecule containing the ketone group at the carbon molecule adjacent to the terminal carbon.

**Maillard browning**—Nonenzymatic, heat-induced browning of foods that occurs over time.

**Maltodextrins**—Nonsweet compounds (DE = 5–20) made from hydrolyzed starches.

**Metabolite**—A substance produced during the metabolism or digestion of a compound.

**Monohydrate**—A compound that contains one molecule of water.

**Monosaccharide**—A carbohydrate containing a single sugar unit, usually composed of five or six carbon atoms, existing in a furanose (five-membered ring) or pyranose (six-membered ring) form.

**Monoterpenoid**—A terpene with one isoprene unit in its structure.

**Phenylketonuria**—Inherited metabolic disease characterized by the inability to metabolize phenylalanine, resulting in brain damage.

**Plastic**—Having a stretchable nature.

**Polydextrose**—A nonsweet polymer of glucose, sorbitol, and citric acid (89:10:1) commonly used to provide bulk in alternatively sweetened foods.

**Polyelectrolyte**—Natural or synthetic substance containing constituents that provide ionic conductivity.

**Polymorphic**—Having the ability to crystallize in more than one three-dimensional arrangement.

**Polyol**—Sugar alcohol, a compound derived from the reduction of sugar.

**Polysaccharide**—A carbon containing several hundred, thousand, or hundred thousand sugar units (from the Greek *poly,* meaning "many").

**Reducing sugar**—A sugar molecule in which the carbonyl group can react to form a carboxylic acid group. The sugar can undergo nonenzymatic (Maillard) browning.

**Refractive index**—Physical property of a substance that relates to how light is refracted from the material. Usually used to indirectly measure some other property, such as soluble solids (i.e., the total sugars in solution).

**Relative sweetness**—Sweetness of a substance compared with that of a reference substance (usually sucrose).

**Short**—Pertaining to the texture of a product that breaks apart very easily when bitten.

**Sucrose**—A 12-carbon disaccharide, composed of one molecule of glucose and one of fructose, obtained from sugar cane and sugar beets; the primary sweetener in the world.

**Surimi**—Japanese word referring to imitation seafood (e.g., crab or lobster) produced by mincing and reforming fish meat along with added flavors.

**Synergistic**—Pertaining to the relationship of two or more ingredients, which combined in a food system have a greater total effect than the sum of the individual effects.

**Terpene**—One of a class of organic compounds that are the most abundant components of essential oils. Terpene structures are segmented into several isoprene units.

**Triterpenoid**—A terpene with three isoprene units in its structure.

**Xylose**—A five-carbon aldo sugar derived from xylan hemicellulose, a by-product of paper pulp manufacture.

# Index